Agaocephalini of the World

세계의 맵시머리장수풍뎅이

최원석 / Wonseok Choi

Esteban Ignacio Abadie

Luis Carlos Pardo-Locarno

Pablo Sebastián Wagner

Stag Lab

사슴벌레연구소

Natural History Science Colletion - Vol. 02
세계의 맵시머리장수풍뎅이
Agaocephalini of the World
발간일 2023년 12월 23일
저자 최원석, 에스테반 이그나시오 아바디, 루이스 카를로스 파르도-로카
르노, 파블로 세바스티안 와그너
편집 제작 김은중
출판 사슴벌레연구소
주소 대전 서구 대덕대로325, 708호, 대한민국
전화 0505-1317-1967
E-mail stag_lab@naver.com
등록 제2022-000014호
ISBN 979-11-981769-2-9 06490
 @최원석

Natural History Science Colletion - Vol. 02
Agaocephalini of the World
Date of Publish 23 DEC 2023
Author Wonseok Choi, Esteban Ignacio Abadie, Luis Carlos Pardo-Locarno, Pablo Sebastián Wagner
Editor/Book Design Eunjoong Kim
Publisher Stag Lab
Address 708 Ho, Daeduk-daero 325, Seo-gu, Daejeon-si, Rep of Korea
Tel 0505-1317-1967
E-mail stag_lab@naver.com
Publisher code 2022-000014
ISBN 979-11-981769-2-9 06490
@Wonseok Choi

Main Author

최원석 Wonseok Choi

Email: won0507won@gmail.com

서울에서 분자바이러스학을 연구하며 석박사통합과정을 밟고 있는 대학원생이다. 어릴 때부터 갖은 생물을 키우고 관찰하기를 좋아했다. 곤충도 역시 그 중 하나였으나, 현실적인 문제로 곤충을 기르기보다 표본을 수집하게 되었다. 전자책으로 '집에서 할 수 있는 식물조직배양'을 출판한 바 있다. 생물학도와 즐거운 이야기를 나눌 기회를 항상 기대하고 있다.

A graduate student who is studying molecular virology in Seoul, South Korea. Since childhood, love to observe and grow various organisms. Insects are one of them, however, due to real life problems, started to collect insect specimens instead. Once published 'Plant tissue culture at home' in e-book format. Always expecting an opportunity to discuss with biologists.

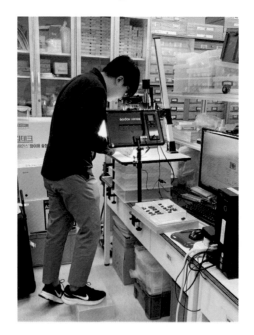

Co-Authors

Luis Carlos Pardo-Locarno, PhD

Email: pardolc@gmail.com

Universidad del Pacifico의 교수이자 연구자이다. 100 편이 넘는 연구를 출판했으며, Scarabaeoidea의 연구를 주로 진행하고 있다. 성충과 유충기를 연구했으며, 현재 Melolonthidae를 연구중이다.

아마추어와 어린 과학자를 돕는데 관심있는 교수로서, 생물학적인 진보와 유충기의 규명에 관심있는 분들의 연락을 환영한다.

Professor and researcher at the Universidad del Pacifico, Colombia. I have published a little more than 100 articles. Many publications in magazines. My biggest area is Scarabaeoidea beetles. I have researched both topics: adults and immature states. I am currently carrying out research in several groups of Colombian Melolonthidae.

I am a professor interested in supporting amateur and young researchers. My contact is available for those who wish to advance biology topics and description of immatures. My email is pardolc@gmail.com, it is an honor to be in this work.

Pablo Sebastián Wagner

Email: wagner@agro.uba.ar

농경학 엔지니어이자 부에노스 아이레스대학의 농경학부 조교수이다. 열정적인 곤충 수집가이며 세계 여러 박물관과 컬렉션의 협력자이다. 전문가들과 다수의 신종을 보고하는 데 함께 작업했다. 'A Field Guide of Long-Horned Beetles from Argentina'의 코오디네이터이자 'a Field Guide of the Dynastidae Family of the South of South America'의 저자이다. 신종을 보고하기 위해, 그리고 다른 곤충학 서적의 출판을 위해 함께 작업하고 있다.

Agronomic engineer, and professor assistants in agronomy Faculty of Buenos Aires [UBA] zoologic area. Passionate collector of insects and collaborator of various museums and collections around the world. Collaborated in descriptions of many new species of insects. Coordinator of the book, a Field Guide of longhorned Beetles from Argentina and coauthor of the A field guide of the dynastidae family of the south of south America. Currently working on the description of new species and publications of insects.

Esteban Ignacio Abadie

Email: estebanabadie@gmail.com

아르헨티나의 곤충학자이다. Agaocephalini를 포함한 갑충류의 여러 신종을 보고했다. 다양한 책과 리뷰의 공저자이자 코오디네이터이다.

Entomologist born in Argentina. An author of descriptions of many new coleoptera species, and also some new Agaocephalini species. A coauthor and a coordinator of many books and genus reviews of Coleoptera.

Publisher

김은중 Eunjoong Kim

대전에서 국립중앙과학관 연구원으로 근무하며 박사학위논문을 준비하고 있다. 최근 주요 관심사는 곤충에 관심있는 사람들이 쉽고 재밌게 볼 수 있는 책을 만드는 것이다.

Based in Daejeon. As a researcher of National Science Museum Korea, now prepareing for his Ph.D thesis. Recent interest is making easy and fun entomology books for insect enthusiasts.

Preface

여유로운 방학의 어느 날이었다. *Chalcosoma*와 톱사슴벌레의 색과 곡선을 좋아하여 상자에 표본을 천천히 모으던 시기였다. 톱사슴벌레를 구경하러 찾아간 박물관에서, 개인이 판매를 부탁한 세계의 장수풍뎅이를 모은 상자를 발견했다. 그 상자에서 만나게 된 첫 Agaocephalini, 금색의 *Spodistes batesi*는 나를 매료시켰다. 그 표본을 구매한 것이 Agaocephalini 수집의 시작이었다.

Agaocephalini는 많은 사람이 그 아름다움을 인정하지만 작은 크기와 희귀함 때문에 인기있는 곤충은 아니었다. 그런 탓인지, 이들에 대한 체계적인 정리는 1985년 Endrödi의 작업 이후 전무했다. 희귀함 때문에 개체의 사진조차 제대로 찾기 어려운 종류가 많았고, 이후 다양한 신종이 보고되었으나 이들에 대한 정보는 접근이 어려웠다. Agaocephalini에 대한 체계적인 정리가 다시 필요함을 느꼈다. 그래서 어느 겨울날, 무작정 다시 한번 책을 펴내는 작업을 시작했다. 논문을 정리하고 리뷰하는 간단한 작업을 생각했지만, 진행할수록 프로젝트는 크고 복잡해졌다. 해외의 연구자, 수집가와 박물관에 도움을 요청하고, 답장을 손꼽아 기다리며, 표본과 사진을 구하기 위해 백방으로 찾아다녔다. 특히나 본업과 저술을 병행하는 것은 쉽지 않은 일이었다. 그럼에도 그 과정에서 *Spodistes angulicollis*의 암컷 개체를 처음으로 보고하는 등 의미 있는 결과를 얻을 수 있었고, 그 최종 결과물을 이렇게 공유할 수 있게 되어 기쁘다. 이후 신비로운 Agaocephalini를 연구하는데 조금이라도 도움이 되기를 바란다.

Spodistes batesi

AGAOCEPHALINI OF THE WORLD

It was a day of relaxing vacation. I was collecting slowly *Chalcosoma* and *Prosopocoilus* since they have beautiful colour and striking curve. The museum where I visited to get *Prosopocoilus* specimens, there was a specific box which contains Dynastinae of the world. In that box, I found my first Agaocephalini, aurulent *Spodistes batesi*. It caught my eyes immediately. I bought it, and it was the beginning of the Agaocephalini collection.

Agaocephalini are considered very attractive beetles among the people, but they are not popular due to its small size and rarity. It may be the reason. In 1985, the publish of Endrödi 'The Dynastinae of the world' is the last systemic organization of Agaocephlini. They are so rare even no images cannot be found on the internet and information is limited although many species are described since 1985. I felt the necessity for systemic review of Agaocephalini. It was the motivation of my work. One day in winter, I thoughtlessly began to write my second book. At the first, I expect simple works like reviewing articles. However, the project becomes larger and more complex. I had to get the aid of researchers, collectors and museums, and looked forward to get an answer from them. In order to obtain images and specimens, tremendous efforts were invested. Furthermore, this time-consuming project was not my main work. Despite that, I could produce valuable results such as finding and reporting the first female individual of *Spodistes angulicollis*, and I am glad to share my work with you. I wish that my work is helpful for studying Agaocephalini, the pulchritude beetles, Agaocephalini.

Remarks

1. 이 책은 현재까지 명명된 Agaocephalini 족의 모든 종을 다룬다.
The book covers all reported species of tribe Agaocephalini.

2. 종의 묘사는 기본적으로 Endrödi(1985)의 기술을 기반으로 한다.
Descriptions of the species are mostly based on Endrödi(1985).

3. Agaocephalini는 전부 중남아메리카대륙에 서식하고 있어, 한국 바깥의 독자를 고려하여 한국어와 영어를 함께 실었다.
 Since Agaocephalini are only distributed in Central and South America, the book is written in Korean and English for readers from outside of South Korea.

4. 저자의 사진이 아닌 경우 하단에서 사진의 제공자를 확인할 수 있다.
 The contributors of images are written on the same page with the images.

5. 지도의 서식 영역은 채집 기록에 기반하여 주 또는 국가단위로 표기하였다.
Distribution maps are based on locality data, depicted as a level of provinces or countries.

Acknowledgement

먼저, 책을 쓰는 동안 지지와 조언을 아끼지 않은 부모님(최철용, 지연순)과 친구 허담에게 특별한 감사를 표한다. 또한 책의 원고를 함께 작업했으며 다양한 사진과 표본을 제공한 PABLO S. WAGNER와 ESTEBAN I. ABADIE, LUIS CARLOS PARDO-LOCARNO 그리고 *Spodistes angulicollis*의 암컷을 함께 규명하고 다양한 정보를 제공해준 RAFAEL SOBRAL ALVES, 책을 출판할 수 있도록 도와주신 김은중님께 많은 감사를 전한다.

또한 아마추어인 저자에게 격려와 조언을 아끼지 않았으며 흔쾌히 사진을 제공해준 황슬마로, 장서준, BRETT C. RATCLIFFE, MARTIN HARDY, KAZUHO KOBAYASHI, LEONELLO MILANI, PATRICK ARNAUD, MASSIMO PRANDI, CALVIN HUANG, CELSO GODINHO JR., EURIDES FURTADO, KIYOTAMI FUKINUKI, FABIEN DUPUIS, 귀중한 표본을 구할 수 있도록 도와준 JAVIER MUÑOZ MILLAN, THOMAS RICHARD, JORGE JENSEN GUZMAN에게 감사를 전한다.

First, I especially thank to my parents, CHOI CHEOLYONG, JI YEONSOON and my friend HEO DAAM, who cordially supported and advised me. I thank to our colleagues, PABLO S. WAGNER, ESTEBAN I. ABADIE, and LUIS CARLOS PARDO-LOCARNO, who provided many images and specimens, also worked on several parts of the book. I thank to RAFAEL SOBRAL ALVES, who describe female of *Spodistes angulicollis* together, and provided much information. I thank to KIM EUNJOONG, who helped to publish this book.

Also, I thank to HWANG SEULMARO, CHANG SEO-JUN, BRETT C. RATCLIFFE, MARTIN HARDY, KAZUHO KOBAYASHI, LEONELLO MILANI, PATRICK ARNAUD, LUIS CARLOS PARDO-LOCARNO, MASSIMO PRANDI, CALVIN HUANG, CELSO GODINHO JR., EURIDES FURTADO, KIYOTAMI FUKINUKI, FABIEN DUPUIS, who supported, advised and provided good images, and JAVIER MUÑOZ MILLAN, THOMAS RICHARD, JORGE JENSEN GUZMAN, who provided valuable specimens.

Contents

Biogeography of Neotropic

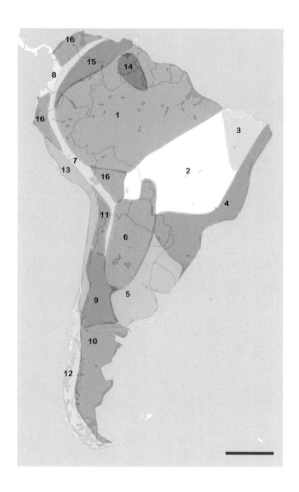

Fig. 1. Map of biomes of South America.

1–Amazonian Rainforest
2– Cerrado
3–Caatinga
4–Atlantic Forest
5–Pampas Grassland
6–Chaco Woodland
7–Cloud Forest and Yungas
8– Choco Wet Forest

9– Monte
10– Patagonian Steppe
11– Puna
12–Chilean or Boreal Forest
13– Desert
14– Upland Guianan Savanna
15– Orinoco Savanna
16– Tropical dry forest

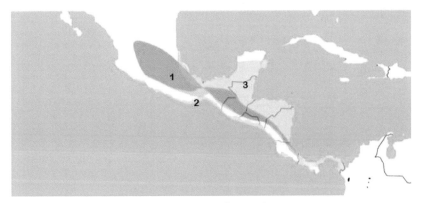

Fig. 2. Map of biomes of Central America.
1-Cloud Forest
2-Tropical Dry Forest
3-Tropical Rain Forest

Agaocephalini족은 남부 멕시코에서 북부 아르헨티나까지 서식한다. 하지만 그 넓은 서식지에서도 일부 생물군계에서만 서식하고 있으며 열대우림의 큰 지역을 차지하는 아마존우림과 같은 생물군계에서는 서식하지 않는다. 많은 종이 두 생물군계가 만나는 지역에 국지적으로 서식한다. 그 중 하나의 예로 *Agaocephala*속이 있으며, 특히 *Democrates croesus*는 캐리비안 지역에 서식하는 반면 *Democrates burmeisteri*는 에콰도르에 서식한다. 이는 캐리비안 지역에 서식하는 지금까지 알려진 유일한 Agaocephalini 종이다.

Agaocephalini가 서식하는 주된 생물군계는 다음과 같다. Cerrado, Atlantic forest, Montane forest, Yungas, Choco wet forest, Aconquija 산맥이다. 각 생물군계를 소개한다.

The tribe Agaocephalini is known from South Mexico to North Argentina. However, in that great range of habitat and territory, they are only distributed in very few biomes and absent in biomes such as Amazonian rain forest, which occupies great region in the neotropics. Many species are endemic in intergrading habitats between two biomes. One example is some species of Agaocephala genus. *Democrates croesus* is distributed in the Caribbean region, but its congener *Democrates burmeisteri* is distributed in Ecuador. It is the only known species of Agaocephalini in the Caribbean.

The main biomes in which we find Agaocephalini species are following. Cerrado, Atlantic forest, Montane forest, Yungas, Choco wet forest, Aconquija mountains. Here, a brief description of the main habitats, where Agaocephalini are found, will be given.

Cerrado

브라질 중부의 넓은 지역과 파라과이 북동부, 볼리비아 남서부의 작은 지역에 위치한 생물군계이다. 작거나 중간 크기의 나무가 자라는 사바나이며, 더 습한 기후가 되면 Cerrado tropical forest 로 발달한다.

불은 이 생물군계 발달에 주요한 요인인데, 불의 영향을 많이 받는 지역은 사바나를 형성하는 경향이 있다 (campo limpo). 이 지역의 기후는 10월부터 3월까지 계속되는 우기를 보인다. 이 생물군계에는 *Aegopsis, Minisiderus, Agaocephala*가 서식한다.

Fig. 3 Cerrado. Minas Gerais, Brazil.
Images courtesy of Pablo Wagner and Esteban Abadie..

It is the biome that located in a big part of central Brazil and small areas in Northeast Paraguay and Southeast Bolivia. It is a Savanna with medium and small trees, in more humid condition it develops into the Cerrado tropical forest.

Fire is an important factor to the development and the areas most affected by fire tends to form a savanna(campo limpo). The climate is tropical with marked rainy season, during October to March. Species of *Aegopsis, Minisiderus* and *Agaocephala* are present here.

Fig. 4. *A. cornigera* on the plant. Pocos de Caldas, Minas Gerais, Brazil.
Images courtesy of Pablo Wagner and Esteban Abadie.

Atlantic Forest

대서양 해변인 리우 그란데 두 노르테 주부터 리우 그란데 두 술까지, 그리고 아르헨티나의 미시오네스와 동 파라과이까지 펼쳐지는 우림이다. 연중 비가 이어진다. 남부의 600 m 이상의 지역에서는 Araucaria forest가 발달한다. 또한 브라질 남동부 대서양림 보호지역은 고도가 800 m를 넘기도 한다. 이는 일반적인 안데스의 숲과 유사하다. 이 생물군계에는 *Agaocephala*와 *Antodon goryi*가 서식한다.

A rain forest, which extends from the atlantic coast of Brazil, Rio Grande do Norte state to Rio Grande do sul, and to Misiones province in Argentina and east Paraguay. The rains occur throughout the year. In high elevations over 600 m on the south part, there are Araucaria forests. Also on the serra do mar side in Brazil, there is a forest whose altitude over 800 m. It is similar to typical cloud forest of Andes. Species of *Agaocephala* and *Antodon goryi* are present here.

Fig. 5. Atlantic forest. Veranopolis, Rio Grande do Sul, Brazil.
Image courtesy of Pablo Wagner and Esteban Abadie.

Montane Forest and Yungas

베네수엘라에서 북부 아르헨티나까지 이어지는 산자락의 습한 숲이다. 아르헨티나 동부와 볼리비아에서 특히 발달한다. 또한 중앙 아메리카에서 멕시코 중부까지도 발달한다.

아르헨티나 지역의 고도는 600 ~ 1400 m이며 에콰도르와 콜롬비아지역에서는 900 ~ 3000 m에 이르러 식생이 더욱 다양하게 발달한다.

이 생물군계에는 *Brachysiderus, Lycomedes, Spodistes, Mitracephala* 그리고 *Democrates* 가 서식한다.

Fig. 6, Yungas, Cristal Mayu, Cochabamba, Bolivia.
Images courtesy of Pablo Wagner and Esteban Abadie.

Fig. 7. Montane forest, Otanche, Boyaca, Colombia.
Images courtesy of Pablo Wagner and Esteban Abadie.

It is a humid forest of the Andes mountain slopes from Venezuela to north Argentina. It is lesser developed on east side of Argentina and Bolivia. Also it extends from central America to central Mexico. Development varies. Altitude in Argentina reaches over 600 to 1400 m, and in Ecuador or Colombia it reaches from 900 to 3000 m, with much greater development and vegetation variety. Species of *Brachysiderus, Lycomedes, Spodistes, Mitracephala* and *Democrates* are present here.

Choco Wet Forest

 600~800 m정도 고도의 태평양쪽 저지대에 주로 분포하며 북서부 에콰도르에서 콜롬비아 서부까지 이어진다. 아메리카 대륙에서 가장 많은 비가 오는 지역으로, 연평균 8000 mm이상의 비가 내리며 특정 지역은 10000 mm를 넘기도 한다. 나무, 야자, 리아나와 나무에 착생하는 식물의 다양성이 매우 크다. *Horridocalia delislei, Spodistes grandis*가 서식한다.

 This is the dominant forest of the pacific lowlands, whose altitude is from sea level 600 to 800 m, from Northwest Ecuador to west Colombia. It is the rainiest region of America, where rainfall exceeds 8000 mm, even 10000 mm annually in some points. The diversity of trees, palms, lianas and epiphytic growth on trees in this forest is very high. *Horridocalia delislei, Spodistes grandis* is present here.

Fig. 8. Rio Anchicaya, Valle del Cauca, Colombia.
Images courtesy of Pablo Wagner and Esteban Abadie.

Aconquija Mountains

투쿠만, 살타, 카타마르카 등 아르헨티나의 북서부 지역에 분포한다. 저지대에는 Chaco woodland, 중간 지역에는 montane forest, Yungas, 2800 m 가 넘는 puna가 있다. 2600 ~ 3300 m 고도에서 *Colacus*가 서식한다.

It is in Tucuman, Salta and Catamarca, Argentina in the northwest region. It is a mountain region with various vegetations such as Chaco Woodland in the lowlands, montane forest or yungas in the middle elevations and puna in highlands over 2800 m. The species of *Colacus* are present here at altitudes from 2600 to 3300 meters.

Fig. 9. Cuesta de Capillitas, Andalgala, Catamarca, Argentina.
Images courtesy of Pablo Wagner and Esteban Abadie.

Tribe Agaocephalini
The history of Agaocephalini

Agaocephalini는 장수풍뎅이아과에 속하는 족[tribe] 중 하나이다. 처음으로 Agaocephala라는 명칭은 1825년 프랑스의 곤충학자 Serville이 새로운 속[genus]으로서 Agaocephala를 발표함으로서 등장했다. 이후 1847년 독일의 곤충학자 Burmeister가 Aegopsis, Agaocephala, Lycomedes, Antodon 네 개의 속을 묶어 Agaocephalidae로 정리했다. 이후 족 수준으로 분류군이 재조정된 것은 1915년 미국의 곤충학자 Casey에 의한 일이었다.

Agaocephalini is one of the tribes belonging to Dynastinae. The taxonomical name 'Agaocephala' first appeared in 1825, by Serville, French entomologist. Later, German entomologist Burmeister organize four genus, Aegopsis, Agaocephala, Lycomedes, Antodon, into Agaocephalidae. In 1915, American entomologist Casey modified the group as the level of tribe.

AGACÉPHALE, *Agacephala*. Ce nouveau genre a été envoyé par M. le baron de Mannerheim à M. le comte Dejean qui a bien voulu nous permettre d'en prendre les caractères dans sa collection. Il appartient à la tribu des Scarabéides et, à ce que nous pensons, à la division des Phyllophages. Voici ce que nous avons aperçu de ses caractères.

Fig. 10. The original description of Agaocephalini.

Le nom d'Agacéphale vient de deux mots grecs et signifie : *tête remarquable*. L'espèce servant de

Fig. 11. The meaning of nomenclature '*Agaocephala*'.

"Agaocephalini" or "Agacephalini"

Agaocephalini의 대표적인 속인 *Agaocephala*는 처음 발표될 당시 '*Agacephala*'로 발표되었다. 그러나 1847년 Agaocephalidae로 정리될 당시에는 '*Agaocephala*'로 표기된 상태였다. 과연 22년 사이에 어떤 일이 일어난 것일까? 어떠한 이유인지는 알 수 없으나, 1829년 핀란드의 곤충학자 Mannerheim은 *Agaocephala*로 기술했고, 이후 거의 모든 학자가 이 이름을 사용하기 시작했다[Smith, A. B., 2006]. 최근에도 *Agacephala*라는 학명이 *Agaocephala*와 혼용되고 있는 실정이다. 이 책에서는 다수가 사용하는 철자를 따라 *Agaocephala*로 표기하였다.

모든 이름에 뜻이 있듯이, 모든 학명에도 의미가 있다. *Agaocephala*는 주목할만한 머리, 위대한 머리와 같은 뜻을 지니고 있다. 이후에 소개될 종들의 머리를 보면 왜 이러한 이름이 붙여졌는지 알아차릴 수 있을 것이다. 저자는 이들의 국명을 '맵시머리장수풍뎅이'로 붙였으나 더 좋은 이름이 있을 것이라 믿는다.

Agaocephala, a representative genus of tibe Agaocephalini, was originally coined '*Agacephala*'. However, in 1847, it is written as '*Agaocephala*' when four genus are grouped into Agaocephalidae. The reason is unknown yet, but in 1829, Finnish entomologist Mannerheim used '*Agaocephala*' instead of '*Agacephala*'. After that, nearly all entomologists have been using '*Agaocephala*'[Smith. A. B. 2006]. Two different names are used with each other even today. In this book, '*Agaocephala*' will be used as it is more common name.

Every name has its own meaning. The term '*Agaocephala*' contains the concept of 'remarkable head', as it can be foud in Fig. 2. You can easily notice why the name is given, if you observe the head of Agaocephalini.

Introduction to tribe Agaocephalini

비교적 작은 분류군인 Agaocephalini는 12개 속과 약 57개 종으로 구성되어 있다. 이들은 오직 중남아메리카 지역에서만 서식하며 대부분은 남아메리카에 분포한다. 이 분류군에 대한 체계적인 조사는 Ratcliffe 교수에 의해 중앙아메리카와 콜롬비아등 일부 남아메리카국가에 한해 이루어졌으며, 브라질, 베네수엘라 등 다른 국가에 대한 조사나 생태 연구는 미비하다.

Agaocephalini is rather small taxonomic group. It consists of 12 genera and about 57 species by far. They inhabit only in Latin America, mostly in South America. A systematic investigated was done by Ratcliffe in limited countries such as Colombia and Central American countries. In the other countries, Brazil and Venezuela for example, investigations are incomplete.

Agaocephalini는 공통된 특징을 분명하게 말하기 어려울 정도로 속 사이의 변이가 크다[Ratcliffe, 2003]. 이 족이 실제로 하나의 계통인지는 추가적인 연구가 필요하며[Ratcliffe, 2003] 하나의 계통이 아니라고 보는 시각 또한 존재한다[Luis, 2020].

The common characteristics of Agaocephalini is hard to describe because of the intragenus variations[Ratcliffe, 2003]. Further investigations are required to evaluate that the tribe is a genuinely single lineage[Ratcliffe, 2003], there is perspective that Agaocephalini is multi-lineage[Luis, 2020].

Agaocephalini의 성충은 대체로 중간 정도의 크기이며, 달걀 모양과 유사하고, 등과 배면[dorsoventral]이 납작한 모양이다. 전미절[propygidium]에는 소리를 내는 영역[stridulatory]이 없고 겉날개에 불규칙한 점각이 있다.

The adults of Agaocephalini is middle-sized, oval-shaped and flattened dorsoventral side. There is no stridulatory area in propygidium and irregular punctures are on the elytra.

이 곤충들이 자연에서 어떻게 생존하는지에 대해서는 유충에 대한 일부 연구와 청정한 숲에서 서식하며 불빛에 이끌려 날아온다는 것을 제외하면 거의 알려진 바가 없다[Moreno, 2019]. 이 분류군은 일부 종을 제외하면 표본으로 만나보기조차 어려울 정도로 희귀하지만, 최근 일본, 대만 등지에서 *A. margaridae*, *S. grandis*, *L. velutipes* 등이 사육되고 있어 유충의 성장 과정에 대해서는 앞으로 더 알려질 것으로 생각된다.

Little is known about the lifecycle and the ecology of these beetles. Only few researches on the larvae have been conducted and it is known that they are attracted to the light[Moreno, 2019]. Although this taxonomic group is extremely rare, few species such as *A. margaridae*, *S. grandis*, *L. velutipes* are breeded as a pet mainly in Japan and Taiwan.

Fig. 12. Representative species of *Lycomedes.*

Aegopsis

Burmeister, 1847

A. bolboceridus
A. chaminadei
A. curvicornis
A. diceratops
A. peruvianus
A. vazdemelloi

Aegopsis

Burmeister, 1847

*Aegopsis*는 여섯 종이 알려져 있다.

묘사. 금속성 광택이 없는 갈색 혹은 검은색이다. 수컷의 이마방패는 둥근데, 양쪽에 뿔이 있다. 반면, 암컷의 경우는 사다리꼴이며 뿔이 없다. 더듬이는 10개의 마디가 있고, 곤봉은 짧다. 수컷의 전흉배판에는 앞을 향한 뿔이 있다. 겉날개는 넓고 짧으며 불규칙적인 점각이 있다. 앞의 경절은 세개 혹은 네개의 이빨이 있다. 뒷 경절은 끝으로 갈수록 넓어지며, 가로지르는 용골모양이 가시와 함께 있다^(Endrődi, 1985).

논의. *Aegopsis*의 생활사는 거의 알려지지 않았고, *A. bolboceridus*의 경우만 기록되었다. 이들은 약 1년의 생활 주기를 가졌으며, 우기에 유충이 자라고 건기에는 휴면한다. 다시 우기가 되면 성충이 우화해 산란한다. 이들은 기주식물의 뿌리를 갉아먹어 해충으로 간주된다^(Sobral, 2018). Burmeister가 *Agaocephala* 중 금속성 광택이 없는 종을 새로운 속으로 분리해 *Aegopsis*가 탄생했다. 모식종인 *A. curvicornis*를 시작으로, Arrow, Dechambre, Grossi, Sobral 등에 의해 다수의 종이 추가되었다.

분포. 코스타리카에서 브라질 중서부까지 서식한다^(Sobral, 2018).

Aegopsis is known as six species.

Description. Black or brown without metallic lustre. Male clypeus rounded. Two horns on either side are developed. Female clypeus trapezoidal and unarmed. Antennae 10 jointed, club short. Male pronotum with forward-directed horn. Elytra broad, short and irregularly punctated. Anterior tibiae with three or four teeth. Hind tibiae dilated to apex with transverse carinae and thorns^(Endrődi, 1985).

Discussion. Little is known about the life cycle of *Aegopsis*. The only species that the life cycle is recorded is *A. bolboceridus*. They have approximately one year of life cycle. Their larvae grow during the rainy season, and diapauses during the dry season. At the beginning of the rainy season, the adults emerge and laying eggs. Since they feed on the roots of plants, *A. bolboceridus* is considered as a pest^(Sobral, 2017). Burmeister considered the non-metallic group of *Agaocephala* as a new genus, *Aegopsis*. Starting with the type species, *A. c*

−urvicornis, many species are described by Arrow, Dechambre, Grossi and Sobral.

Distribution. Costa Rica to mid−west Brazil[(Sobral, 2017)].

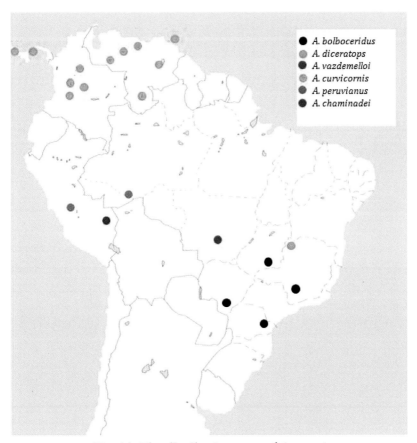

Fig. 14. The distribution map of Aegopsis.

*Aegopsis*의 검색표

1. - 앞 경절은 4개의 이빨이 있다..*curvicornis*
1' - 앞 경절은 3개의 이빨이 있다..2

2. - 머리뿔의 기부는 휘어진 용골구조로 연결된다. 삽입기 양 옆의 용골구조는 옆에서 보았을 때 끝 부분까지 이어지지 않는다...............................*peruvianus*
2' - 머리뿔의 기부를 잇는 용골구조가 없다. 삽입기 양 옆의 용골구조는 옆에서 보았을 때 끝 부분까지 이어진다...3

3. - 삽입기의 끝은 기부보다 좁다. 하순기절은 둥글다......................*chaminadei*
3' - 삽입기의 끝은 기부의 두 배 이상 넓다. 하순기절은 사각형 혹은 삼각형 모양이다...4

4. - 이마방패 끝은 둥글다. 안각은 앞으로 튀어나온다. 하순기절의 끝 부분 모서리는 용골구조다..*diceratops*
4' - 이마방패 끝은 뭉툭하거나 약하게 톱니모양이다. 안각은 튀어나오지 않는다. 하순기절은 용골구조가 없다...5

5. - 전흉배판의 뒷 모서리에는 미세한 점각이 없다. 턱은 끝 부분의 돌기가 바깥쪽 용골구조와 가깝다. 하순기절은 사각형이다. 삽입기는 옆에서 보았을 때 phalobase의 끝보다 좁다...*bolboceridus*
5' - 전흉배판의 뒷 모서리에는 미세한 점각이 있다. 턱은 끝 부분의 돌기가 없다. 하순기절은 삼각형이다. 삽입기는 옆에서 보았을 때 phalobase의 끝만큼 두껍다.
....*vazdemelloi*

Fig. 15. *Aegopsis diceratops*

Key to species of *Aegopsis*

1. – Protibia with four external teeth...*curvicornis*
1' – Protibia wirh three external teeth..2

2. – Base of cephalic horns connected by a curved carina. Lateral carina of parameres not reaching apex of parameres in lateral view................*peruvianus*
2' – Base of cephalic horns with no connecting carina. Lateral carina of parameres reaching apex of parameres in lateral view....................................3

3. – Apex of parameres less than one time longer than base of parameres. Mentum round...*chaminadei*
3' – Apex of parameres about two times longer than base of parameres. Mentum subrectangular or subtriangular..4

4. – Clypeus with round apex. Ocular canthi protruding anteriorly. Apical corners of mentum carinate...*diceratops*
4' – Clypeus apex truncate or slightly emarginate. Ocular canthi not protruding. Mentum lacking carina..5

5. – Punctures on posterior angles of pronotum with no micropunctures between them. Mandibles with apical protuberance near external carina. Mentum subrectangular. Parameres, in lateral view, narrower than apex of ph alobase...*bolboceridus*
5' – Punctures on posterior angles of pronotum with micropunctures between them. Mandibles with no apical protuberance. Mentum subtriangular. Parameres, in lateral view, almost as thick as apex of phalobase...*vazdemelloi*

Fig. 16. *Aegopsis curvicornis*

Aegopsis bolboceridus

(Thomson, 1860)

묘사. 사각형에 가깝고 끝 부분이 직선이며 중간 부분이 살짝 톱니모양으로 오목한 이마방패를 가진다. 앞에서 보았을 때, 머리의 뿔은 조금 벌려져 있고 가로로 굽었다. 안각은 뿔의 기부와 조금 떨어져 있고, 바깥 모서리 부분은 앞쪽으로 쭉 뻗었다. 하순기절은 신장되어 사다리꼴에 가깝고 옆은 구불구불하며, 중앙에서 보았을 때 끝 부분은 쭉 뻗었다. 생식기는 위에서 바라볼 때 끝 부분이 작고 옆의 용골이 기부에서 거의 L 모양으로 분명하게 꺾인다. 밑에서 바라볼 때, 배 면의 용골은 기부와 끝이 뾰족하며 ostium의 아래쪽 가장자리가 약하게 오목하다^(Sobral, 2018).

분포. 브라질 Cerrado의 넓은 지역에 서식하고 있다^(Sobral, 2018).

Description. Clypeus subrectangular with straight, slightly emarginated apex. In frontal view, cephalic horns moderately open and laterally angled. Ocular canthus slightly detached from the base of horns and the outer edge anteriorly straight. Mentum is elongated, subtrapezoidal, sinuous on the sides. Apex straight in the middle. In dorsal view, the apical region of paramere compact, lateral carina curved distinctly towards the apex. In lateral view, lateral carinae curved at the base, almost "L" shape. In ventral view, ventral carinae are basally acuminate and its apex pointed. The lower edge of ostium slightly concave^(Sobral, 2018).

Distribution. Widely distributed in Brazil, Cerrado^(Sobral, 2018).

Remark

이 종은 브라질에서 해충으로 여겨진다^(De Oliviera, 2008).

This species is considered as pests in Brazil^(De Oliviera, 2008).

Brazil, 30.5 mm

Fig. 17. *Aegopsis bolboceridus*

Aegopsis chaminadei

Dechambre, 1999

묘사. 수컷의 이마방패는 사각형이고 끝 부분이 둥글며 약간 오목하게 들어가 있다. 앞에서 보았을 때 머리 뿔은 중간 정도로 열려 양 옆으로 각져있다. 안각은 뿔의 기부에서 약간 떨어져 있다. 거의 직선이며, 뒷 부분의 가장자리가 각져있거나 앞부분의 가장자리가 굽어있다. 중간 부분은 오목하게 들어가 있다. 하순기절은 작고 둥그런 모양이며 옆이 강하게 볼록하다. 윗입술은 등 쪽에서 보아 뒷 부분으로 오목하고 중앙에서 앞부분으로 직선이다. 위를 향하는 로브 두 개가 있고 옆으로는 조금 가늘어진다. Maxillary palpomere IV는 짧고 타원형이며, 감각 부위가 크고 물방울 모양이다. 생식기는 등 쪽에서 보아 바깥 가장자리가 넓고 끝을 향해 강하게 굽었다. 옆에서 보았을 때, 용골은 기부에서 둥글다. 끝 부분은 무디다. Ostium의 아래 부분의 가장자리는 크게 오목하다[Sobral, 2017].

진단. *A. chaminadei*는 *Aegopsis*에서 가장 특이한 종이다. 몸의 특징은 *A.bolboceridus*와 매우 비슷하지만, 생식기와 입의 구조 일부, 서식지는 이 종이 *A. peruvianus*와 유사한 것을 나타내기 때문이다. 이 종은 *A. peruvianus*와 유사한 다른 종과 다음의 특징으로 구분된다. 턱이 작고, 옆이 둥글고, 신장 모양의 galea, palpomere IV의 기부에서 시작하는 더 짧고 넓은 감각 부위, 뿔을 연결하는 용골, 사각형 이마방패, 이마방패를 살짝 넘어서는 가슴 뿔, 생식기의 모양 등이다. 또한, *A. bolboceridus*와는 턱, galea, 감각 부위 등이 다르다[Sobral, 2017].

논의. Dechambre는 1999년 이 종을 발표할 당시 한 개체의 암컷을 묘사하고 MNHN에 보관하였다고 기술했는데, 해당 종의 암컷 표본은 MNHN에 존재하지 않는다[Sobral, 2017].

분포. 페루에 서식한다.

Description. In males, the clypeus is subrectangular and has rounded, slightly emarginated apex. In frontal view, the cephalic horns are moderately open and laterally angled. The ocular canthus is slightly detached from the base of the horn. It is almost straight and the outer edge is posteriorly angled or anteriorly curved, and emarginated in the middle. The mentum is compact, rounded and convex on the sides. In dorsal view, the labrum is posteriorly concave, anteriorly straight in the middle. There are two lobes projecting upwards. Laterally, it is slightly tapered. The maxillary palpomere IV is short and ellipsoid with a large, drop-shaped sensory area. In dorsal view, the paramere has broad outer edge that is strongly curved towards the apex. In lateral view, the lateral carina is rounded at the base. The apex is blunt. The lower edge of the ostium is strongly concave[(Sobral, 2017)].

Diagnosis. *A. chaminadei* is peculiar species because characteristics of the body are very similar to *A. bolboceridus* group. However, its genitalia, some traces of mouth parts and the distribution indicate that *A. chaminadei* belongs to *A. peruvvianus* group. It differs from the other species in *A. peruvianus* group by compact and laterally rounded chin, reniform galea, shorter and wider sensory area starting at the base of palpomere IV, absence of the carina connecting the base of the horns, prothoracic horn slightly exceeding the clypeus, shape of parameres and others. It also differs from *A. bolboceridus* group by the shape of chin, galea, the sensory area and others[(Sobral, 2017)].

Discussion. In the orginal description by Dechambre(1999), a single female is depicted and it is mentioned that the specimen is deposited in the MNHN. However, there is no female type specimen in the MNHN[(Sobral, 2017)].

Distribution. Peru[(Sobral, 2017)].

Fig. 18. *Aegopsis chaminadei*, Paratype

Image courtesy of Kazuho Kobayashi.

Fig. 19. *Aegopsis chaminadei*, Paratype

Aegopsis curvicornis
Burmeister, 1847

Aegopsis westwoodi Thomson, 1860
Aegopsis atra Sternberg, 1904
Aegopsis nigricollis Sternberg, 1904
Aegopsis rubricollis Sternberg, 1904
Aegopsis trinidadensis Sternberg, 1904

묘사. 항문상판의 디스크는 빛나고, 미세하고 드문 점각이 있다. 털은 없다. 전흉배판과 겉날개는 어두운 갈색이다. 노란 빛을 띄는 개체는 nigricollis, 완전히 검은 색을 띄는 대체는 atra로 부르기도 한다. 이마의 뿔은 휘어져 있고 단면이 삼각형이다. 턱은 덮여 있다. 전흉배판의 옆은 미세하고 밀도있게 주름져있다. 중앙 부분은 작고 드문 점각이 있다. 앞의 경절은 네 개의 강한 이빨이 있다^(Endrödi, 1985).

분포. 파나마, 콜롬비아, 에콰도르, 베네수엘라, 트리니다드, 브라질에 서식한다^(Endrödi, 1985).

Description. Disc of pygidium very shining with fine, sparsely punctated and bare. Elytra dark brown. The specimens with yellowish elytra are called nigricollis, or the pronotum is much darker or black, it is called atra. Frontal horns curved and cross-section triangular. Mandibles are covered. Sides of pronotum with fine, dense wrinkles. In the middle, very fine and sparse punctures. Protibia with four strong teeth^(Endrödi, 1985).

Distribution. Panama, Colombia, Ecuador, Venezuela, Trinidad and Brazil^(Endrödi, 1985).

Remark

이 종은 *A. westwoodi*라는동물이명으로 주로 거래된다.

This species is usually traded under the name of synonym as *A. westwoodi*.

Merida, Venezuela, 27.5 mm

Fig. 20. *Aegopsis curvicornis*

Aegopsis diceratops

Sobral & Grossi, 2017

묘사. 수컷의 이마방패는 사각형에 가깝고 끝 부분이 둥글다. 오목하게 들어간 부분은 없다. 앞에서 보았을 때, 머리의 뿔은 약간 열려있고 양 옆으로 둥글다. 안각은 중앙 부위의 가장가리가 앞쪽으로 돌출되어있다. 하순기절은 길고 사다리꼴 모양이며 양쪽이 살짝 볼록하다. 위에서 보는 labrum은 앞으로 곧고 양 옆은 뾰족하다. 위에서 보는 생식기는 끝 부분이 얇으며 양옆의 용골이 분명하게 끝으로 휘어있고 밑의 기부는 강하게 위로 올라가 J처럼 보인다. 배면의 용골은 기부가 둥글고 끝이 뾰족하다. ostium의 아랫 부분은 강하게 오목하며 조금 뾰족한 모양을 만든다. 양 옆은 경계가 조금 모호하다[(Sobral, 2018)].

논의. 특히, 쉽게 드러나는 차이점으로 *A. bolboceridus*와는 돌출된 안각, 톱니모양으로 오목하지 않은 이마방패로 구분할 수 있다. 암컷은 사다리꼴 모양의 이마방패, 강한 이마의 돌기, 가늘어지지 않고 털이 많은 항문상판으로 구분된다. 고이아스에서 파라나까지 서식하는 *A. bolboceridus*와 서식지가 겹치지만, 지금까지 이 종은 북서부 미나스 제라이스의 900m 고도 rupestrian field에서만 관찰되었다. 마치 바다와 같은 역할을 하는 강이나 매우 다른 식생환경을 가진 지역이 Cerrado를 여러 지역으로 나눈다. 이러한 장벽이 종의 분화를 야기한다는 이론이 제시되었으며, *A. diceratops*와 *A. bolboceridus*가 이와 같은 경우일 수 있다. 실제로 이 두 개체군이 분리되어 있는가를 확인하기 위해서는 더 많은 연구가 필요하다[(Sobral, 2018)].

Description. Male clypeus subrectangular with slightly rounded apex, not emarginated. In frontal view, cephalic horn slightly open and rounded laterally. Outer edge of eye canthus protrudes anteriorly in the middle. Mentum elongated, subtrapezoidal with slightly convex sides. In dorsal view, labrum anteriorly straight and acuminated on the sides. In dorsal view, paramere apex thin, lateral carinae distinctly curved towards the apex. In lateral view, lateral carinae evidently curved at the base and the base strongly elevated, thus it has a "J" shape. In ventral view, ventral carinae basally rounded with acuminaetd apex. Lower edge of ostium strongly concave and moderately acuminated. Sides oblique[(Sobral, 2018)].

Discussion. Especially, following characteristics are identification keys of *A. diceratops* that separate it from *A. bolboceridus*. The shape of protruding canthus, non-emarginated clypeus. Females can be distinguished by the trapezoidal clypeus, strong frontal tubercle and non-tapered and heavily hirsute pygidium. *A. diceratops*, distributed from Goias to Parana, shares its habitats with *A. bolboceridus*. However, *A. diceratops* have been found in the rupestrian field, northwestern Minas Gerais, at altitude of 900 m. It has been proposed that the valleys or distinct phyto-physiological areas serve as a barrier between mountains, like islands separated by ocean. More research is required to confirm that *A. bolboceridus* and *A. diceratops* are truly isolated populations[(Sobral, 2018)].

Fig. 21. *Aegopsis diceratops*

A. bolboceridus Clypeus

A. diceratops Clypeus

A. bolboceridus Eye Canthus

A. diceratops Eye Canthus

Fig. 22. Clypeus, eye canthus of *Aegopsis diceratops* beside to *A. bolboceridus*

Aegopsis peruvianus

Arrow, 1941

묘사. 항문상판의 디스크는 그물모양이며 거의 평평하다. 밀도있는 점각이 있으며 기부의 반은 짧고 드문 강모가 나있다. 머리와 전흉배판의 뿔은 대부분 약하다. 가장 작은 수컷의 경우 이마에 깔대기 모양의 짧은 뿔이 있을 뿐이다. 앞 경절에는 세 개의 이빨이 있다. 생식기는 매우 다르게 생겼다. 바깥쪽이 강하게 굽었고, 끝 부분은 거의 날카롭다[Endrödi, 1985].

논의. 최근까지 이 종은 뿔이 짧은 수컷만 채집되었지만, Sobral(2017)은 긴 뿔을 가진 개체를 채집하여 그 특징을 기록하였다. 이마방패, 안각, 생식기를 이용해 *A. peruvianus*로 동정한 이 개체로 턱 부위에 대한 특징이 기록되었다.

분포. 페루와 브라질에 서식한다[Sobral, 2017].

Description. The disc on the pygidium is reticulated and nearly mat. There are dense punctures and sparse setae are present on the basal half. The armature of the head and the pronotum is mostly weak. In the smallest male, the frontal horns are just short and conical shape. The protibia has three teeth. The paramere is very different. The outer side is strongly curved, and the apex is almost sharp[Endrödi, 1985].

Discussion. Until Sobral(2017), only short-horned males are collected. However, Sobral(2017) described the characters of the mouth parts using long-horned individual. It is identified as *A. peruvianus* by the clypeus, ocular canthus, paramere.

Distribution. Peru to Brazil[Sobral, 2017].

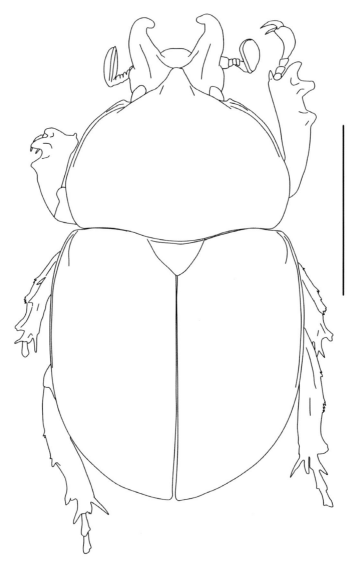

Fig. 23. *Aegopsis peruvianus*

Aegopsis vazdemelloi
Sobral & Grossi, 2017

묘사. 수컷의 이마방패는 사각형을 닮았으며 끝 부분이 둥글고, 살짝 톱니모양으로 오목한 부분이 있다. 앞에서 본 머리의 뿔은 강하게 열려있고 양 옆으로 각겨있다. 안각은 뿔의 기부와 거의 연결되어 있으며 바깥쪽 가장자리는 앞을 향해 살짝 둥글다. 턱은 길고, 사다리꼴과 닮았으며, 옆에서 각겨있고 중앙에 둥근 첨단이 있다. Labrum은 등에서 보아 앞을 향해 볼록하고 중앙이 살짝 돌출되며 양 옆이 가늘다. 생식기는 등에서 보았을 때 끝 부분은 얇고 양옆의 용골이 굽어 조금 급하게 끝을 향한다. 옆에서 보았을 때, 양옆의 용골은 기부에서 꺾여 "J" 모양을 만든다. 배면에서 보면, 배면의 용골이 기부와 끝부분 모두 뾰족하고, ostium의 아랫쪽은 어느정도 오목하며 뾰족한 모양이다[Sobral, 2018].

논의. *A. vazdemelloi*는 안각의 모양, 암컷의 이마 결절, 생식기의 모양이 *A. bolboceridus*와 크게 유사하다. 그러나 *A. vazdemaelloi*의 이마방패가 더 둥글고, labrum의 앞쪽이 볼록하며 중간에서 돌출되어 있으며, 생식기의 바깥 가장자리가 끝을 향해 더 각겨있다는 점에서 두 종이 구분된다. 암컷은 더 길고 앞부분이 덜 연결되어 있는 안각과 조금 더 두드러진 이마 결절로 구분할 수 있다. 이 종은 마토 그로소의 Cerrado지역인 Chapada dos Guimaraes에서만 발견되었다. 이 지역은 더 습하고 강가 숲의 면적이 더 넓은데, 이러한 환경의 개체군이 *A. vazdemelloi*로 분화했을 수 있다[Sobral, 2018].

Description. Male clypeus subrectangular with rounded, slightly emarginated apex. Cephalic horn, in frontal view, strongly open and laterally angled. Eye canthus almost continuous with the base of horns and outer edges slightly rounded anteriorly. Mentum elongated, subtrapezoidal and angled at the sides. In the middle of mentum, apex rounded. In dorsal view, labrum with tapered sides is anteriorly convex and slightly protruded in the middle. In doesal view, apical region of parameres thin. Lateral carina curved at the base in a "J" shape. In ventral view, ventral carina acuminated at the base and apex. The lower edge of ostium concave, acuminated.

Discussion. *A. vazdemello*i resembles *A. bolboceridus* due to its shape of eye canthus, the frontal tubercle of females, the shape of the parameres. However, the clypeus of *A. vazdemelloi* is more rounded, and the labrum is anteriorly convex and protruded in the middle. The parameres of *A. vazdemelloi* is slightly angled at the outer edge towards apex. The females are distinguished by more elongated and anteriorly-poorly connected ocular canthus, and more prominent frontal tubercles. This species is found only at the Chapada dos Guimaraes, an area of Cerrado in the state of Mato Grosso. This region is generally more humid and extensive area of valley forests is present. The population in this specific region might be differentiated into *A. vazdemelloi*[(Sobral, 2018)].

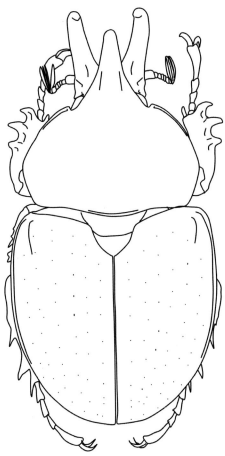

Fig. 24. *Aegopsis vazdemelloi*

Agaocephala

Serville, 1825

A. bicuspis
A. brasiliana
A. cornigera
A. duponti
A. inermicollis
A. mannerheimi
A. margaridae
A. melolonthida
A. urus

Agaocephala

Serville, 1825

*Agaocephala*는 아홉 종이 알려져 있다.

묘사. 머리, 전흉, 소순판 그리고 배면은 금속성 녹색, 초록색, 혹은 파란 색 광택이 있다. *A. brasiliana*를 제외하면 곁날개는 갈색이며 약간의 금속 광택이 있다. 수컷의 경우 머리에 두 개의 뿔이 있거나 뾰족하지만 암컷의 경우는 없다. 턱은 두 개의 이빨이 있다. 더듬이의 곤봉은 나머지 10개의 관절의 길이와 비슷하거나 더 길기도 하다. 전흉배판은 항상 길기보다는 넓다. 수컷에게는 전흉배판에 앞으로 뻗은 뿔 혹은 혹이 있는데, 일부 종은 암컷처럼 아무런 뿔이 없기도 하다. 곁날개의 점각은 불규칙하며 주름이 있기도 하다. 앞의 경절은 세 개 혹은 네 개의 이빨이 있고, 뒤의 경절은 끝으로 갈수록 넓어진다. 수컷의 앞 부절에서, 안쪽 발톱은 바깥쪽보다 더 발달되어 있다[Endrödi, 1985].

Agaocephala is known as nine species.

Description. The head, prothorax, scutellum and abdomen has metallic green, red or blue lustre. The elytra is brown with weak metallic lustre except *A. brasiliana*. The head of males have two horn or simply acuminated but in females, it is unarmed. The mandibles have two teeth. The clubs of antennae are as long as all other ten joints or longer. The pronotum is always broader than long. In the males, there is forward-directed horn or big conical knob on the pronotum. However, in some species including *A. bicuspis*, *A. duponti* and etc., it is unarmed like females. Elytra is irregularly punctated, often wrinkled. The anterior tibiae have three or four teeth. The hind tibiae are dilated to apex. The inner claws of anterior tarsi are more developed than the outer claws[Endrödi, 1985].

Fig. 25. The distribution map of *Agaocephala*.

Fig. 26A. Poços de Caldas,
Minas Gerais, Brazil
Agaocephala duponti,
Image courtesy of Celso Godinho Jr.

Fig. 26B. Poços de Caldas,
Minas Gerais, Brazil
Agaocephala cornigera,
Image courtesy of Celso Godinho Jr.

*Agaocephala*의 검색표

A. *melolonthidae*는 제외되었다.

1. - 겉날개는 벨벳같다...*brasiliana*
1' - 겉날개는 벨벳같지 않다...2

brasiliana

2. - 가슴뿔이 없다...3
2' - 가슴뿔이 있다...5

without horn

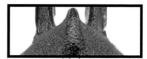

with horn

3. - 앞 경절의 이빨은 뭉툭하고, 겉날개에 주름이 없다.............................*bicuspis*
3' - 앞 경절의 이빨은 날카롭고 겉날개에 주름이 있다.............................4

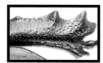

bicuspis

to 4

4. - 전흉배판은 강하고 밀도있게 점각이 있다.............................*duponti*
4' - 전흉배판은 빛나고 점각은 약하다.............................*inermicollis*

duponti

inermicollis

5. – 가슴뿔의 끝은 두 갈래로 나뉜다...6
5' – 가슴뿔의 끝은 두 갈래로 나뉘지 않는다...7

bifurcated

not bifurcated

6. – 가슴뿔은 짧고 가늘다. 머리뿔은 기부가 넓다.....................................*urus*
6' – 가슴뿔은 길고 두껍다. 머리뿔의 기부는 좁다..........................*mannerheimi*

urus

mannerheimi

7. – 전흉배판은 둥글고 머리뿔은 평행하다...*cornigera*
7' – 전흉배판의 앞의 양 옆 모서리가 뾰족하다. 머리뿔은 이빨이 있고 강하게 휘
어진다...*margaridae*

cornigera

margaridae

A. MELOLONTHIDAE는 제외되었다.

Key to species of *Agaocephala*

Identification Keys, *A. melolonthidae* is omitted.

1. – Elytra velutinous...*brasiliana*
1' – Elytra not velutinous...2

brasiliana

2. – Pronotum without a horn...3
2' – Pronotum with a horn...5

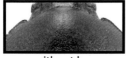
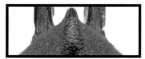

without horn　　　　　　　　　　**with horn**

3. – Teeth on protibiae blunt, no wrinkles on elytra...........................*bicuspis*
3' – Teeth on protibiae acute, wrinkles on elytra.................................4

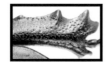

bicuspis　　　　　　　　**to 4**

4. – Pronotum densely and strongly punctate.....................................*duponti*
4' – Pronotum shiny, with weak punctate.....................................*inermicollis*

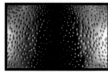

duponti　　　　　　　　*inermicollis*

5. – Pronotal horn bifurcated at the apex...6
5' – Pronotal horn not bifurcated at the apex...............................7

bifurcated

not bifurcated

6. – Pronotal horn short, thin, cephalic horn with wide base.....................*urus*
6' – Pronotal horn long and thick, cephalic horn with narrow base.......*mannerheimi*

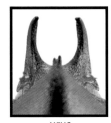

urus

mannerheimi

7. – Pronotum round, cephalic horn parallel....................................*cornigera*
7' – Anterior lateral angles of pronotum acute, cephalic horn with teeth strongly curved..*margaridae*

cornigera

margaridae

Agaocephala bicuspis
Erichson, 1858

묘사. 전흉배판과 겉날개는 색이 옅다. 미세한 주름이 있으며 밀도있고 크기가 서로 다른 동그런 점각이 있다. 머리는 두 개의 짧은 뿔이 있고, 전흉배판은 거의 뿔이 없다고 볼 수 있다. 겉날개는 갈색이며 녹색의 금속성 광택이 있다. 겉날개의 길이는 드물게 넓이보다 조금 더 길다. 항문상판은 짧고, 기부가 강하게 볼록하며, 앞부분의 반은 배 아래로 후퇴해 있다. 앞쪽의 경절은 네 개의 이빨이 있다[Endrödi, 1985].

분포. 베네수엘라에 서식한다.

Description. Pronotum and elytra nearly pale and finely wrinkled with dense and unequal annular punctures. Elytra metallic green lustre. Scarcely longer than broader. Head with two short horns. Pronotum nearly unarmed. Pygidium short and strongly convex base, posterior half is retracted under the abdomen. Anterior tibiae with four teeth[Endrödi, 1985].

Distribution. Venezuela.

Bolivar, Venezuela, 30 mm

Bolivar, Venezuela, 27 mm

Fig. 27. *Agaocephala bicuspis*

Agaocephala brasiliana

Martinez & Alvarenga, 1987

이 종은 아속^(subgenus) *Lycocephala*에 속하는 유일한 종이다.

묘사. 일반적인 외형은 *Agaocephala*와 같으나 다음과 같은 특징으로 구분된다. 전흉배판의 양 옆 가장자리가 톱니모양이고, 강한 점각이 있다. 겉날개는 회색의 털이 빽빽하고, 머리와 전흉배판은 등 쪽에서 볼 때 더욱 확실히 털이 많다. 수컷의 경우, 뒷 경절은 양옆에 이빨이 없고, 내부 가장자리를 따라 많은 긴 털이 있다^(Martinez, 1987).

논의. 해당하는 아속 *Lycocephala*는 이러한 특징으로 *Agaocephala*와 쉽게 구분되며, 외형으로 보아 *Agaocephala*와 *Lycomedes*의 중간 형태로 추정하고 있다^(Martinez, 1987).

분포. 브라질의 바이아에 서식한다.

A. brasiliana is the only species of subgenus *Lycocephala*.

Description. The general appearance is same as *Agaocephala* but it differs by following characteristics. The lateral edge of the pronotum is denticulated, and the pronotum is strongly punctated. The elytra is tomentose with grayish hair and it is more apparent when observe in dorsal view. In males, the posterior tibiae are without lateral teeth and the internal margin is with very long and bush hair^(Martinez, 1987).

Discussion. *Lycocephala* is easily distinguishable by mentioned characters. It would be an intermediate species between *Agaocephala* and *Lycomedes*^(Martinez, 1987).

Distribution. Bahia, Brazil.

Remark

*A. brasiliana*의 표본은 그 개수가 매우 적다. 최근 브라질에서의 박물관 화재로 유실되기도 하였다. 야생에서는 절멸했을 가능성이 제기된다.

The specimens of *A. brasiliana* is extremely rare, recent fire at Brazilian museum cause the loss of the valuable specimen of this species. It is possible that the species is extinct in the wild.

Image courtesy of Pablo Wagner and Esteban Abadie

Image courtesy of Kiyotami Fukinuki

Fig. 28. *Agaocephala brasiliana*

Agaocephala cornigera
Serville, 1825

묘사. 머리에 있는 두 뿔은 평행하며 기저에서 하나로 합쳐지는데, 높은 용골모양을 이룬다. 전흉배판의 혹은 짧다. 머리와 전흉배판은 녹색 광택이 있다. 이마방패는 넓게 잘린듯한 모양이며 오목하게 들어가 있다. 항문상판은 매우 강하게 볼록하고, 배 아래로 후퇴해 있다. 앞의 경절은 세 개의 이빨이 있으며 드물게 네 번째 이빨의 흔적이 보인다. 안쪽의 발톱이 바깥쪽의 것 보다 강하게 발달해있다(Endrödi, 1985, Serville, 1825).

분포. 브라질의 미나스 제라이스, 리우 데 자네이루에 서식한다(Endrödi, 1985, Serville, 1825).

Description. Two horns of head parallel, connected at the base, which forms high carina. Knob of pronotum short. Clypeus broadly truncated and emarginated. Pygidium very strongly convex and retracted under abdomen. Anterior tibiae with three teeth but rarely have a trace of fourth tooth. Inner claw developed stronger than outer ones(Endrödi, 1985, Serville, 1825).

Distribution. Minas Gerais, Rio de Janeiro, Brazil(Endrödi, 1985, Serville, 1825).

Minas Gerais, Brazil, 34 mm

Fig. 29. *Agaocephala cornigera*

Agaocephala duponti

Castelnau, 1832

묘사. 원기재문에서 강한 점각으로 묘사할 만큼 전흉배판의 가운데에도 강한 점각이 있다. 녹색 혹은 붉은색이 감도는 갈색 광택이 있다. 전흉배판의 앞쪽 가장자리의 뒤에 작은 돌기가 있다. 수컷의 항문상판은 강하게 볼록하고, 끝 부분은 드물게 배 아래로 후퇴해 있다. 앞쪽의 경절은 세 개의 이빨을 가지는데, 암컷의 경우는 네 개이다. 두 개의 검은 반점이 겉날개에 있다(Endrödi, 1985, Castelnau, 1832).

분포. 미나스 제라이스, 상파울로, 리우 데 자네이루에 서식한다(Abadie, 2008).

Description. Very strong punctures, even in the middle of the pronotum, as its original description depicts it 'very punctated'. Brown with greenish or reddish lustre. Behind the anterior margin of the pronotum, a small tubercle presents. Pygidium strongly convex and scarcely retracted under the abdomen. Anterior tibiae with three teeth but females with four teeth. Two black spots on the shoulder of elytra(Endrödi, 1985, Castelnau, 1832).

Distribution. Minas Gerais, Sao Paulo, Rio de Janeiro, Brazil(Abadie, 2008).

32. Agacephala Duponti.

Valdè punctata, nitide viridis, elytris fuscis, marginibus, sutura basi dilatata, et maculis duabus singulorum, nigris.

Fig. 30. The original description of *A. duponti.*

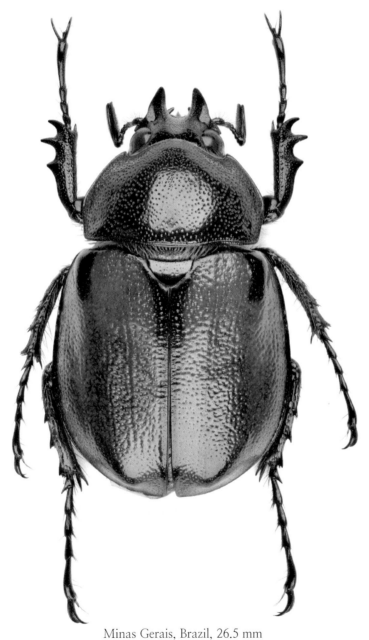

Minas Gerais, Brazil, 26.5 mm

Fig. 31. *Agaocephala duponti*

Agaocephala inermicollis
Arrow, 1914

묘사. *A. duponti*와 유사한 종이다. 하지만 Arrow는 *A. duponti*는 물론 *Agaocephala*의 모든 종과 '특히 전흉배판이 부드럽고 빛나는 표면을 가지고 있다'는 점에서 차이를 나타낸다고 보았다[Arrow, 1914]. 또한 가슴에 뿔을 가지지 않은 네 종류 중 하나이다. 전흉배판에는 매우 미세하고 드물게 점각이 있는데, 중앙일수록 심하며 가장자리 근처에 좁은 점각이 있다. 양 옆의 가장자리는 주름져있다. 빛나는 적색 혹은 녹색 광택을 가지고 있고, 겉날개는 갈색이고 불규칙적인 점각이 있다. 뿔은 짧다. 항문상판은 강하게 볼록하고, 끝 부분은 배 아래로 후퇴해 있다. 앞의 경절은 세 개의 이빨을 가진다[Endrődi, 1985].

분포. 리우 그란데 두 술의 포르투 알레그레, 상파울루, 브라질과 Quebrada de los Cuervos, 우루과이에 서식한다.[Endrődi, 1985] [Ratcliffe, 2023].

Description. It is closely related to *A. duponti*. Arrow concluded that *A. inermicollis* differs from all of other species of *Agaocephala* by the following characteristic. It has smooth and shining surface, that of the pronotum especially. Also, it is the one of the three species that have no trace of thoracic process[Arrow, 1914]. Pronotum very finely and sparsely punctated, especially in the middle. Only near the margins, bigger and shallow punctates. Lateral margins very finely wrinkled. Shining metallic red of green. Elytra brown, with irregular punctures. Horns short. Pygidium strongly convex and the apex retracted under the abdomen. Protibiae with three teeth[Endrődi, 1985].

Distribution. Porto Alegre, Rio Grande do Sul, and Sao Paulo in Brasil and Quebrada de los Cuervos, Uruguay.[Endrődi, 1985], [Pablo Wagner].

Sao Paulo, Brazil, 25 mm
Fig. 32. *Agaocephala inermicollis*

Agaocephala mannerheimi

Castelnau, 1832

묘사. 전흉배판에 강하고 앞으로 뻗어나온 뿔이 있으며, 끝부분은 두갈래로 갈라진다. 머리와 전흉배판은 거의 평평하다. 금속성의 구리색이며, 겉날개는 금속성의 녹색 광택이 있다. 이마방패는 넓게 잘린듯한 모양이다. 겉날개는 미세한 점각이 점각 크기의 몇 배 정도의 간격을 두고 있다. 항문상판은 강하게 볼록하고, 끝 부분은 배 아래로 후퇴해 있다. 앞의 경절은 세 개의 이빨을 가진다. 뒤의 경절은 가로지르는 용골과 이빨이 있다(Endrödi, 1985).

분포. 브라질의 고이아스, 미나스 제라이스, 마토 그로소 두 술, 아르헨티나의 미시오네스에 서식한다(Endrödi, 1985, Abadie, 2008).

Description. Pronotum with strong, forward, bifurcated horn. Head and pronotum nearly mat. Metallic brown and elytra with metallic green lustre. Clypeus broadly truncated. Elytra punctated which intervals are several times broader than diameter of punctates. Pygidium strongly convex and the apex retracted under the abdomen. Protibiae with three teeth. Metatibiae toothed, with transverse carinae(Endrödi, 1985).

Distribution Goias, Minas Gerais, Mato Grosso do Sul, Brazil and Misiones, Argentina(Endrödi, 1985, Abadie, 2008).

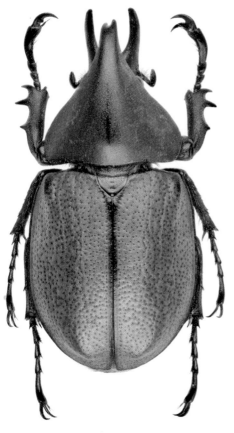

Minas Gerais, Brazil, 39 mm

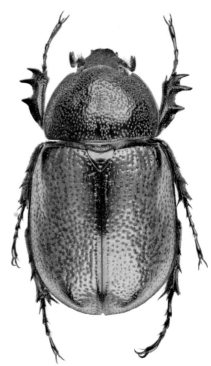

Minas Gerais, Brazil, 28 mm

Fig. 33. *Agaocephala mannerheimi*

A.mannerheimi in the habitats

Fig. 34A. Vale da Solidão, Diamantino, Mato Grosso, Brazil
Images courtesy of Eurides Furtado

Fig. 34B. Vale da Solidão, Diamantino, Mato Grosso, Brazil
Images courtesy of Eurides Furtado

Agaocephala margaridae

Alvarenga, 1958

묘사. 뿔은 얇고 길며, 중간쯤에 큰 내치가 있다. 전흉배판의 혹은 짧고 원뿔모양이다. 머리와 전흉배판은 구리색이며 경절과 부절은 붉은색에 가깝다. 이마방패의 끝 부분은 오목하다. 대형 수컷은 뿔의 길이가 전흉배판의 길이와 비슷한 정도이다. 항문상판의 끝 부분은 배 아래로 후퇴해 있다. 앞의 경절은 네 개의 이빨이 있고, 뒤의 경절은 두 개의 가로지르는 용골과 하나의 큰 이빨이 있다[Endrödi, 1985].

분포. 브라질의 파라에 서식한다[Endrödi, 1985].

Description. Horn thin and long, and strongly toothed in the middle. Pronotal knob short and conical. Head and the pronotum bronze. Tibiae and the tarsi metallic red. Apex of clypeus emarginated. In the case of large male, the horns are as long as the pronotum. Apex of pygidium retracted under the abdomen. Protibiae with four teeth, metatibiae with two transverse carina and one strong tooth.[Endrödi, 1985]

Distribution. Para, Brazil[Endrödi, 1985].

Remark

A. *margaridae*의 서식지는 파괴되지 않았으나 개체수는 줄고 있다. Grossi는 그 원인으로 모기를 통제하기 위한 살충제를 지적하고 있다[Grossi, 2008].

The habitats of A. *margaridae* is conserved, but the populations decline. Grossi has pointed out that the insecticides used to control mosquitoes might be the cause[Grossi, 2008].

Para, Brazil, 45 mm

Fig. 35. *Agaocephala margaridae*

Para, Brazil, 32 mm

Fig. 36. *Agaocephala margardiae*

AGAOCEPHALINI OF THE WORLD

Agacephala
margaridae
n.

M. Alvarenga det. 1958

Cachimbo(E.Pará)
Travassos-Oliveira
& Adão, 25/9-10-956

Paratipo

BRASIL,PA,Cachimbo,Base
da Aeronáutica,25/9.X.1956
Travassos, Oliveira &
Adão Legs.

Fig. 37. *A.margaridae* Paratype

Images courtesy of Massimo Prandi,
The specimen belongs to Massimo Prandi collection, Italy.

Agaocephala melolonthida

Thomson, 1860

묘사. 수컷이 알려지지 않았다. Endrödi는 그의 1985년 저술에서 파란색 광택이 있고 겉날개가 갈색이라는 점만 명시했다. 이 종의 원기재문에서는 다음과 같이 묘사하고 있다. 머리 중앙에 크게 오목한 구멍이 있고 뿔이 없으며 밀도있게 점각이 있다. 전흉도 역시 뿔이 없으며 소순판에는 강한 점각이 있다. 항문 상판에도 밀도있는 점각이 있다. 이러한 색깔과, 머리와 전흉의 형태 그리고 더 강하고 밀도있는 점각, 커다란 더듬이의 곤봉에서 차이가 있다고 보았다. 브라질에 서식한다고 기록되었다[Endrödi, 1985, Thomson, 1860].

Description. The male is unknown. Endrödi only noted that 'Metallic blue and elytra is brown' in his publish in 1985. The original description of *A.melolonthida*, however, depicts this species as following. The head is largely excavated, unarmed and densely punctated. The pronotum unarmed, and the scutellum has strong puncta. The pygidium has strong and dense puncta, too. Thomson concluded that it is differ from other species because of the color, appearance of head and pronotum, stronger and denser punctates, and the big club of antennae. It is recorded in Brazil[Endrödi, 1985, Thomson, 1860].

Remark

이 종은 최초 보고 이후 발견되지않았다. 해당 종의 존재가 의심스러운 상황이다.

This species has never been found after the original description. It is suspicious about the existence of the species.

Fig. 38. Original drawing of *A. melolonthida*

Thomson, 1860

Agaocephala urus

Thomson, 1860

묘사. *A. mannerheimi*와 유사하지만, Thomson은 다음과 같은 점에서 다르다고 보았다. 색이 다르고, 머리의 뿔이 더 작고 짧으며, 겉날개의 점 각이 덜 발달해있고, 특히 몸체가 덜 볼록하다[Thomson, 1860]. 두 뿔 사이에는 용골이 존재하지 않고 바로 내려온다. 머리와 전흉배판은 녹색 광택이 있 다. 겉날개는 허술하게 그물모양이며 거의 평평하다. 항문상판의 끝 부분 은 배 아래로 후퇴해 있다. 앞의 경절은 세 개의 이빨이 있고, 안쪽의 발 톱이 바깥쪽의 것 보다 두꺼우며 작은 가시가 분명하다[Endrödi, 1985].

분포. 브라질의 이스피리투 산투, 미나스제라이스에 서식한다[Endrödi, 1985].

Desrciption. It is similar to *A. mannerheimi*, but Thomson concluded that it is different because of following characteristics. The color is different, the horns of head are minor and short, the punctures of elytra are less developed, particularly the body is less convex[Thomson, 1860]. The head between horns are only declivous. There are no carinae. The head and the pronotum has green lustre. The elytra roughly reticulated and nearly mat. The pygidium retracted under the abdomen. The protibiae has three teeth. The inner claws are thicker than outer ones, and the toothlet is distinct[Endrödi, 1985].

Distribution. Espirito Santo, Minas Gerais, Brazil[Endrödi, 1985].

AGAOCEPHALINI OF THE WORLD

Minas Gerais, Brazil, 26 mm

Fig. 39. *Agaocephala urus*

Antodon

Breme, 1844

A. goryi

Antodon

Breme, 1844

오직 한 종만이 알려져 있다.

묘사. 수컷의 머리엔 세 갈래로 나뉘어진 뿔이 있고, 암컷에게는 없다. 소순판은 삼각형이며, 겉날개는 넓고 불규칙적인 점각이 있다. 앞쪽의 부절은 두꺼우며, 안쪽의 발톱이 바깥쪽보다 크다. 앞의 경절에는 세 개의 이빨이 있고, 뒤의 경절은 끝을 향해 약하게 넓어지는 모양새다[Endrödi, 1985].

It is known as only one species.

Description. A trifurcated horn is on the head of males, but the head of females are unarmed. Scutellum triangular. Elytra broad and with irregular puncta. Anterior tarsi of males thickened, and inner claw bigger than outer one. Protibiae with three teeth, metatibiae dilated weakly toward apex[Endrödi, 1985].

Fig. 40. The distribution map of Genus *Antodon*.

Antodon goryi

(Castelnau, 1832)

Agacephala goryi Castelnau, 1832
Antodon burmeisteri Breme 1844

묘사. 머리, 전흉, 소순판은 녹색 금속 광택이 난다. 이마방패는 매우 짧고 넓게 잘린 모양이다. 전흉배판은 양 옆으로 길며 옆이 강하게 휘었다. 매우 강하고 밀도있는 점각이 있다. 겉날개의 길이는 너비와 비슷하며, 양옆이 굽어있고, 동그란 점각들이 불규칙하게 있다. 미절은 강하게 볼록하나, 암컷에선 평평하다[Endrödi, 1985]. 원기재문에서는 매우 점각이 있고, 구리빛이며, 날개는 황토색이고, 가슴의 양 옆은 톱니 모양이며, 더듬이와 부절은 검은색으로 표현하고 있다[La Porte, 1832].

분포. 브라질의 리우 데 자네이루, 미나스 제라이스, 이스피리투 산투에 서식한다[Endrödi, 1985].

Description. Head, prothorax and scutellum greenish metallic lustre. Clypeus very short, broadly truncated. Pronotum broad, sides strongly curved, and strongly and densely punctated. Elytra broad as long as, sides are curved, and small, annularly and irregularly punctated. Pygidium strongly convex, but in female, flat[Endrödi, 1985]. The original description depicts it as very punctuated, copper-coloured, elytra ochre, thorax laterally crenulated, antennae and tarsi black[La Porte, 1832].

Distribution. Rio de Janeiro, Minas Gerais, Espirito Santo, Brazil[Endrödi, 1985].

---

33. Agacephala Goryi.

Valdè punctatissima, cupreo-ænea; elytris ochraceis; thoracis lateribus crenulatis; antennis tarsisque fuscis.

Fig. 41. The original descripton of *Antodon goryi*.

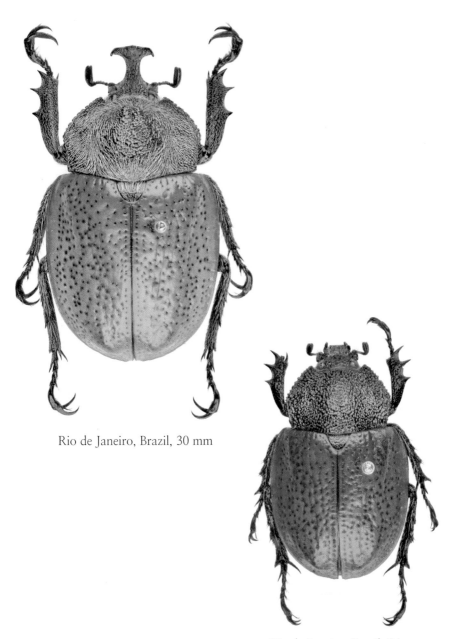

Rio de Janeiro, Brazil, 30 mm

Rio de Janeiro, Brazil, 24 mm

Fig. 42. *Antodon goryi*

Brachysiderus

Waterhouse, 1881

B. q. quadrimaculatus
B. q. tridentiger

Brachysiderus
Waterhouse, 1881

*Brachysiderus*는 1개 종의 2개 아종으로 이루어져 있다.

묘사. 금속 광택이 없는 갈색이다. 머리에는 긴 두 갈래로 갈라지는 뿔이 있다. 턱은 이마방패로 덮인다. 더듬이는 10마디로 이루어져 있고 곤봉마디는 짧다. 전흉배판은 볼록하거나 끝 부분 뒤에 두 개의 결절이 있다. 겉날개에는 봉합선이 있고 불규칙적으로 점각이 있다. 전미절에는 소리를 내는 기관이 없다. 앞 경절은 세 개 혹은 네 개의 이빨이 있다[Endrödi, 1985].

Brachysiderus is known as one species and two subspecies.

Description. Brown without metallic lustre. Head of male with long bifurcated horn. Mandibles covered by the clypeus. Antenna ten jointed and club short. Pronotum convex or with two tubercles behind the apical margin. Elytra with sutural stria and irregular punctae. Propygidium without stridulatory area. Protibia with three or four teeth[Endrödi, 1985].

Key to subspecies of *Brachysiderus*

1.- Elytra finely reticulated, shiny, strongly and densely punctate. Northwestern Brazil and Eastern Peru......................*quadrimaculatus*

1'.- Horn with a middle-apical acute process. Elytra strongly reticulated, oily, more sparsely and finely punctate than quadrimaculatus. Western Ecuador, Western Peru and Bolivia. ....*tridentiger*

quadrimaculatus

tridentiger

Fig. 43. Identification keys

Fig. 44. The distribution map of *Brachysiderus*.

Brachysiderus quadrimaculatus

B. quadrimaculatus quadrimaculatus Waterhouse, 1881

묘사. 노란 갈색을 띠며 양 어깨에 검은 점이 있다. 봉합선과 혹의 끝 부분도 검은색이다. 수컷의 머리에는 긴 두갈래의 뿔이 있다. 안각은 작고 뿔의 앞과 위를 향하게 발달한다. 전흉배판은 간단하게 볼록하다. 수컷의 앞의 부절은 두껍고, 안쪽 발톱이 강한 이빨을 가진다. 앞 경절은 세 개의 이빨을 가진다. 겉날개가 미세하게 그물모양이며 강하고 밀도있는 점각이 있다[Endrödi, 1985].

분포. 페루 동부와 브라질에 서식한다[Endrödi, 1985].

Description. It is yellowish brown with humeral black dot. The suture and the apex of knob is black. The long, bifurcated horn is on the head of males. The canthus in males produces into a small, forward and upward directed horn. The pronotum is simply convex. The anterior tarsi of males are strongly thickened. The inner claw has strong tooth. The protibia has three teeth. The elytra is finely reticulated and strongly, densely punctated[Endrödi, 1985].

Distribution. Eastern Peru and Brazil[Endrödi, 1985].

B. quadrimaculatus tridentiger Prell, 1934

Lycotharses tridentiger Prell, 1934
Agaocephala breyeri Martinez, 1963

묘사. 겉날개가 강하게 그물모양이며 점각이 드물고 미세하다[Endrödi, 1985].

분포. 에콰도르, 페루 서부의 안데스, 볼리비아에 서식한다[Endrödi, 1985].

Description. The elytra is strongly reticulated and sparsely, finely punctated[Endrödi, 1985].

Distribution. Ecuador, Andes of West Peru and Bolivia[Endrödi, 1985].

Iquitos, Peru, 40 mm

Fig. 45. *B. quadrimaculatus quadrimaculatus*

Guanay, Bolivia 35 mm

Figure 46. Male *B. quadrimaculatus tridentiger*

Guanay, Bolivia, 34 mm

Figure 47. Female *B.quadrimaculatus tridentiger*

Colacus

Ohaus, 1910

C. bicolor
C. cuchimilco
C. morio
C. moroni
C. rubrofemoratus

Colacus

Ohaus, 1910

Cyclocephalini, 그리고 *Democrates, Gnathogolofa*[Moreno, 2015]와 연관된 이 단순하게 생긴 장수풍뎅이는 다섯 개의 종으로 구성되어 있다.

묘사. 이마방패는 삼각형 모양으로 늘어나 있고 이마에는 결절이 있다. 바깥쪽이 단순하게 굽은 큰 턱은 강하게 튀어나와 있다. 더듬이는 10개의 관절과, 그 관절만큼 긴 곤봉으로 이루어진다. 부절은 매우 얇다. 전흉배판은 단순히 오목하다. 겉날개는 밀도 있게 점각이 있으며 약하게 두 개의 점열이 있다[Endrödi, 1985].

분포. 북서부 아르헨티나의 High Monte, Central Andean Puna생태지역에 세 종이 서식하며 최근 브라질, 페루에서 신종이 발견되었다[Sobral, 2019].

A simple Dynastinae, closely related to *Cyclocephalini, Democrates* and *Gnathogolofa*[Moreno, 2015], consists of five species.

Description. Clypeus elongate triangular, frons with tubercle. Mandibles strongly projected and outside curved simply. Antennae ten-jointed, club as long as joints. Tarsi very thin. Pronotum simply convex. Elytra densely punctated and weak double rows of punctures are marked[Endrödi, 1985].

Distribution. In northwestern Argentina, three species are known from High Monte and Central Andean Puna. Recently, new species are described from Brazil and Peru[Sobral, 2019].

Fig. 48. The distribution map of *Colacus.*

*Colacus*의 검색표

Fig. 49. *Colacus* sp.

Key to species of *Colacus*

1. Head, pronotum, and elytra black ·· 2

1'. Head and pronotum black, elytra light reddish brown or yellowish brown

··· 4

2. Cephalic tubercle emarginate. Femora ventrally dark reddish brown.

··· *rubrofemoratus*

2'. Cephalic tubercle entire, not emarginate. Femora ventrally black ········ 3

3. Protibia tridentate. Pronotum with shallow, subapical fovea ········· *morio*

3'. Protibia quadridentate. Pronotum evenly convex, lacking shallow,

subapical fovea ·· *cuchimilco*

4. Clypeal apex acute. Labium slightly convex in lateral view, apex with 2

small projections ··· *bicolor*

4'. Clypeal apex nearly truncate. Labium strongly convex in lateral view, apex

lacking 2 small projections ··· *moroni*

AGAOCEPHALINI OF THE WORLD

Colacus bicolor

Ohaus, 1910

묘사. 겉날개는 빛난다. 미세하고 밀도있게 점각이 있으며 점각 사이의 간격은 점각보다 크다. 미절은 약하게 볼록하고 빛난다. 앞의 경절은 세 개의 이빨이 있다. 뒤의 경절은 부분이 약하게 부풀어있고 끝의 가장자리 부분이 약 12개의 털과 함께 잘린 모양이다. 가로지르는 용골모양 구조가 강하다[Endrödi, 1985].

분포. 아르헨티나의 투쿠만, 카타마르카에 서식한다[Endrödi, 1985].

Description. Elytra shiny. Puncta fine and dense, interval bigger than the puncta itself. Pygidium slightly convex and shiny. Protibiae with three teeth. Apex of metatibiae weakly dilated and apical margin truncated with about 12 bristles. Transversal carinae strong[Endrödi, 1985].

Distribution. Tucuman and Catamarca, Argentina[Endrödi, 1985].

Salta, Argentina, 20 mm

Fig. 50. *Colacus bicolor*

Colacus cuchimilco
Figueroa and Ratcliffe, 2023

묘사. 이마에는 낮고 둥근 가로지로는 돌기가 있다. 안각은 둥글고 양 옆으로 동출되지 않았지만 끝 부분은 각져있다. 이마방패는 아래로 휘었고, 안각까지 닿은 용골 모양을 가진다. 앞 경절은 4개의 이빨이 있다. 몸 전체가 검은 색이다.

분포. 페루의 리마에 서식한다.

Description. Frons with low, transverse, round tubercle at center. Eye canthus round, not projected laterally, apex acute. Clypeus deflexed, cariniform, carina extends to clypeus. Protibia quadridentates. Entire body black.

Distribution. Lima, Peru.

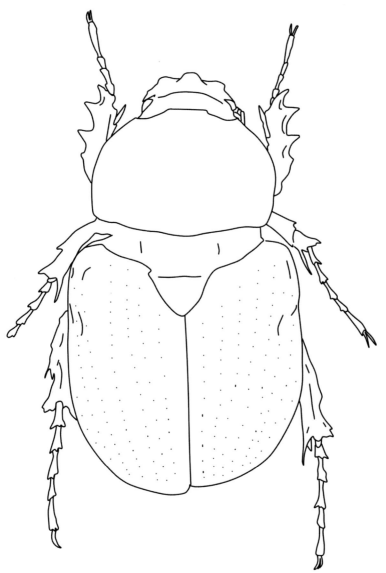

Fig. 51. *Colacus cuchimilco*

Colacus morio

Ohaus, 1910
Colacus endroedii Martinez, 1988

묘사. 등과 배면이 완전한 검은색이다. 이마방패는 좁아지는 모양으로 끝은 잘려 휘어진 모양이다. 표면은 주름져있고 강모는 없다. 뿔의 뒤쪽은 약하게 오목하다. 전흉배판은 약하게 티나는 두 개의 로브가 있어 앞쪽에 작은 오목한 부위를 만든다. 뒷 경절은 짧은 강모가 없고, 뒷 퇴절은 부풀어 있지 않다. 미절은 기부에 눈알무늬가 있고 측면 끝까지 닿는 강모가 있다[(Moreno, 2015)].

분포. 아르헨티나, 투쿠만에 서식한다.

Description. Dorsal and ventral colour entirely black. Clypeus declined and apex truncated and flexed. Surface rugose without setae. Posterior of horn area slightly concave. Pronotum with slightly marked lobes form anterior fovea. Metatibia without short setae. Metafemur not dilated. Pygidium basally ocellated and setae extends to lateral edges[(Moreno, 2015)].

Distribution. Tucuman, Argentina.

Fig. 52. *Colacus morio*

Image courtesy of B. C. Ratcliffe, University of Nebraska, USA

Colacus moroni

Neita-Moreno, 2015

묘사. 2015년 발표된 이 종은 다음과 같은 특징으로 구별된다. 이마방패는 톱니 모양이고, 약간 휘었으며 표면에는 얇고 짧은 강모가 있다. 측면에서 보았을 때 입술은 크게 볼록하고, 측설은 발달해있지 않다. 중간과 뒷 경절의 안쪽 기부에는 짧은 가시 같은 선이 없다. 미절은 기부에 눈알무늬가 있고 끝 부분까지 닿는 강모가 있다. 가운데 디스크는 끝이 부드럽고, 불규칙적인 점각이 있다. 측면에서 볼 때, *C. bicolor*보다 더 볼록하다[(Neita-Moreno, 2015)].

분포. 아르헨티나, 투쿠만에 서식한다.

Description. This species, described in 2015, differs from other species of genera by the following characteristics. Apex of clypeus truncated and slightly flexed. Short, thin setae are on the surface. The labium is strongly convex in lateral view. Paraglossae is not developed. On the inner basal face of meso- and metatibiae, spiniform lines are absence. The basal of pygidium is ocellated and setae extends to lateral edges. The apex of median disk is smooth. Few punctates are irregularly distributed. It is more convex than *C. bicolor* in lateral view[(Neita-Moreno, 2015)].

Distribution. Tucuman, Argentina.

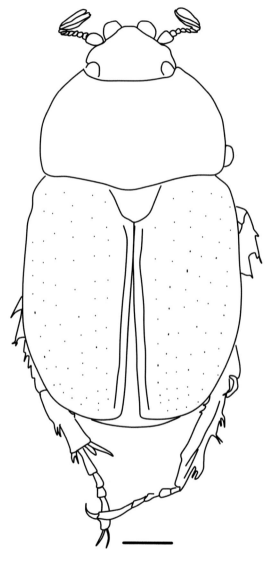

Fig. 53. *Colacus moroni*

Colacus rubrofemoratus
Sobral, Morais & Grossi, 2019

현재까지 밝혀진 Colacus 종 중, 유일하게 브라질에 서식한다^{(Sobral, Morais} ^{& Grossi, 2019)}.

묘사. 머리에 끝이 두 갈래로 갈라지는 결절을 가지고 있다. 다른 종류는 원뿔 모양의 끝이 뾰족한 결절을 가진다. 다리가 붉다. 큰턱은 볼록해 거의 타원모양이다. 안각은 직각이다^(Sobral, Morais & Grossi, 2019).

분포. 브라질, 미나스 제라이스 북부에 서식한다.

Among the Colacus species, this is the only species which inhabits in Brazil^(Sobral, Morais & Grossi, 2019).

Description. Cephalic tubercle emarginated. The other species have a conical tubercle with a sharp apex. Legs red. Mandibles convex, almost semicircular. Ocular canthus rectangular^(Sobral, Morais & Grossi, 2019).

Distribution. Northern Minas Gerais, Brazil.

Fig. 54. *Colacus rubrofemoratus*
Image courtesy of Fabien Dupuis.

Democrates

Burmeister, 1847

D. burmeisteri
D. croesus

Democrates

Burmeister, 1847

*Democrates*는 총 두 종이 알려져 있다.

묘사. 이마방패는 잘린 듯한 모양이다. 머리와 전흉배판에는 뿔이 없다. 턱은 어느정도 튀어나와있고 바깥 면은 간단하게 굽어있다. 더듬이는 10개의 관절이 있는데, 곤봉은 그 관절들의 길이와 비슷하다. 전흉은 길기보다는 넓다. 전미절은 미세하게 가로지르는 점각이나 단순한 점각이 있다. 앞 경절은 세개의 이빨이 있다. 뒷 경절은 끝으로 갈수록 두꺼워진다. 앞의 부절은 약하게 두꺼우며, 모든 발톱이 똑같이 생겼다[Endrödi, 1985].

Democrates is known as two species.

Description. Clypeus truncated. Head and ptonotum unarmed. Mandibles moderately projected and outer sides simply convex. Antenna ten jointed. Club as long as all other joints. Prothorax broad. Propygidium either transversely and finely punctated or simply punctated. Protibiae tridentate, the metatibiae dilated to the apex. Protarsi are weakly thickened. All claws are equal[Endrödi, 1985].

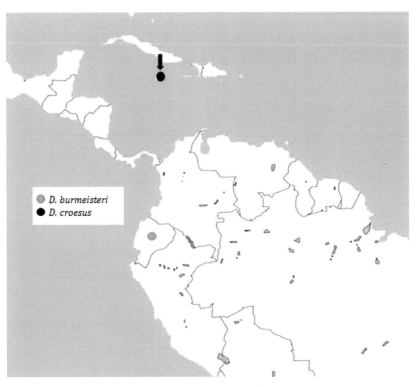

Fig. 55. The distribution map of *Democrates*.

Democrates burmeisteri

Reiche, 1852

Democrates lepiouffi Dechambre, 2006

묘사. 이마방패의 옆면은 끝부분 쪽에서 톱니모양이다. 부절이 매우 얇다. 앞 부절의 발톱과 연결되는 부위는 그 뒤의 부절 3개의 길이와 같다. 전미절은 매우 미세하고 밀도있게 점각이 있다[Endrödi, 1985].

동정. 이 속의 다른 종인 *D. croesus*와 비슷하게 생겼지만 색이 더 어둡고 머리와 전흉배판은 거의 검은색이다. 또한 겉날개가 더 길고 점각이 더 많으며 미세하다. 좁은 주름으로 두 개의 열이 보인다[Endrödi, 1985].

분포. 에콰도르에 서식한다[Endrödi, 1985].

Description. Sides of clypeus emarginated before apex. Tarsi very thin. Claw-joint of protarsi in male as long as three following joints. Propygidium punctated densely and finely.

Diagnosis. This species is similar to the other species of the genera, *D. croesus*, but colours are darker, the head and the pronotum are nearly black. Also, the elytra is longer and more finely and densely punctated. The double rows are marked by shallow furrows[Endrödi, 1985].

Distribution. Ecuador[Endrödi, 1985].

Fig. 56. *Democrates burmeisteri*

Image courtesy of
B. C. Ratcliffe, University of Nebraska, USA

Democrates croesus

Newman, 1836

묘사. 수컷의 이마방패는 길고 위를 향하며 암컷은 부등변사각형 모양이다. 부절은 강하다. 부절과 발톱을 잇는 관절의 길이는 나머지 관절의 길이와 같다. 전미절은 매우 드물고 가로지르게 점각이 있다. 붉은 빛이 도는 갈색이고 빛난다. 전흉배판과 날개 기부 사이의 공간은 노란 강모로 가득 차있다. 미절의 기부와 배면의 표면은 노란 털이 있다. 그 이외의 표면은 털이 없다. 머리는 주름지고 점각이 있다. 전흉배판의 기부는 중앙에서 살짝 돌출되는데, 경계가 뚜렷한 디스크가 있고 디스크는 미세하고 드물게 점각이 있다. 그 외에는 더 강한 점각이 보인다. 겉날개는 넓기보다는 길다. 미세하고 밀도 있게 점각이 있다[(Endrödi, 1985)].

분포. Endrödi는 그의 저서에서 이 종이 Antiles에 서식한다고 했으나, 자메이카 이외의 섬에서 확인된 적은 없다[(Ratcliffe, 2011)].

Description. Male clypeus long and upturned. That of female trapezoid. Tarsi strong. Claw-joint of protarsi in male as long as all other joints. Propygidium sparsely and transversely punctated. The colour is reddish brown and shining. The area between pronotum and the basis of elytra is beset with yellowish setae. Basis of the propygidium and sternum with yellowish setae. Elsewhere surface bare. Head wrinkled and punctated. Basis of pronotum produced at the middle, disc with distinct border. Disc very sparsely and finely punctated. In the front and the sides more densely punctated. Elytra not much longer than broader. Puncta moderately dense and fine[(Endrödi, 1985)].

Distribution. Endrödi noted that this species inhabits in Antiles but specimens from this region never found except Jamaica[(Ratcliffe, 2011)].

Fig. 57. *Democrates croesus*
Image courtesy of
B. C. Ratcliffe, University of Nebraska, USA

Gnathogolofa

Arrow, 1914

G. bicolor

Gnathogolofa

Arrow, 1914

비교적 크고 넓적한 종인 *Gnathogolofa*는 오직 한 종만이 알려져 있다.

묘사. 이마방패는 끝으로 갈수록 좁아지고, 이마에는 짧은 뿔이, 암컷에게는 작은 돌기가 있다. 턱은 앞으로 튀어나와 넓으며 바깥쪽에 이빨은 없다. 더듬이관절은 10개로 이루어져 있고, 곤봉은 작다. 겉날개는 망상모양이며 미세한 점각이 드물게 있다. 전미절에는 소리를 내는 기관이 약하게 발달해있다. 앞 경절은 세 개의 이빨이 있고 뒷 경절은 끝으로 갈수록 확장된다[Endrödi, 1985].

Gnathogolofa, rather big and broad species, is known as only one species.

Description. Clypeus narrow to apex. On the frons, male with short horn and female with tubercle. Mandibles strongly projected and broad, without outer teeth. Antenna ten jointed, and club short. Elytra reticulated and finely and sparsely punctated. Propygidium with weak stridulatory area. Protibiae tridentated. Metatibia dilated to apex[Endrödi, 1985].

Fig. 58. The distribution map of *Gnathogolofa*.

Gnathogolofa bicolor

Ohaus, 1910

묘사. 배쪽의 표면은 검은색이지만 전흉배판은 노랗고 빛난다. 전흉배판의 앞 경계면의 바로 뒤에 검은색 영역이 있다. 표면에는 털이 없고 미절과 배쪽에는 털이 많다. 이마방패의 끝부분은 잘린 듯한 모양이고 전흉배판의 옆면은 규칙적으로 굽어있어 기부는 중간에서 살짝 튀어나오고 앞경계면의 뒤에는 작은 혹이 있다. 미절은 볼록하며 미절 판은 미세하고 드물게 점각이 있다[Endrödi, 1985].

분포. 에콰도르에 서식한다.

Description. Ventral sternites black but the pronotum yellow and shiny. Behind the anterior margin of pronotum with black spot. Surface bare but the basis of pygidium and sternum setose. Clypeus truncated. The sides of pronotum regularly curved, basis slightly produced in the middle and knob is behind the anterior margin. Pygidium convex, discs finely and sparsely punctated[Endrödi, 1985].

Distribution. Ecuador.

Azuay, Ecuador, 29.5 mm

Fig. 59. *Gnathogolofa bicolor*

Horridocalia

Endrödi, 1974

H. delislei

Horridocalia

Endrödi, 1974

*Horridocalia*는 오직 한 종이 알려져 있다.

묘사. 턱의 끝 부분은 깊고 넓게 톱니모양이다. 더듬이는 10마디로 이루어지는데, 곤봉은 짧다. 전흉배판의 끝부분 가장자리 뒤에는 높은 혹이 있다. 겉날개는 점열이 있다. 전미절의 중간 부분에는 매우 짧은 가로지르는 날[edge]이 있다. 항문상판은 짧다. 앞 경절에는 세 개의 이빨이 있고, 뒷 경절은 끝으로 갈수록 넓어진다. 앞의 부절은 조금 두꺼워져 있으며, 안쪽 발톱이 강하게 굽어있다[Endrödi, 1985].

논의. *Horridocalia*는 'horridus'와 해당 종이 발견된 곳의 지명 'Cali'의 합성어로, '칼리의 야수'라는 의미이다[Endrödi, 1974].

Horridocalia is only known as single species.

Description. Mandibles emarginated deeply and broadly at the apex. Antenna ten jointed and the club short. Elytra punctated in a row. In the middle part of propygidium, with extremely short transversal edges. Pygidium short. Protibia tridentated. Metatibia weakly dilated to the apex. Protarsi moderately thickened. Inner claw strongly curved[Endrödi, 1985].

Discussion. *Horridocalia* is a compound word of 'horridus' and 'Cali', where the specimen is found. It means 'Beast of Cali'[Endrödi, 1974].

Fig. 60. The distribution map of *Horridocalia*.

Horridocalia delislei

Endrödi, 1974

묘사. 검고 빛나며, 표면의 몇 곳은 갈색 털이 구름처럼 나있다. 이마방패는 짧은 삼각형모양이다. 이마의 뿔은 길고, 깊게 둘로 갈라져 있으며, 위로 휘었다. 전흉배판의 혹은 넓고 높다. 앞 쪽의 반은 옆면이 날카로운 용골모양이며, 끝 부분은 둥글면서 약하게 톱니모양을 가지고 비슷하게 용골모양이다. 겉날개를 포함한 표면은 둥근 점각이 많다. 점각은 마지막 디스크에서 미세하고 가장자리에서는 강해진다^(Endrödi, 1985).

분포. 에콰도르와 콜롬비아에 서식한다^(Endrödi, 1985, Ratcliffe, 2011).

Description. Black and shining. Several places of its surface nebulously tomented with brown hair. Clypeus shortly triangular. Frontal horn long, deeply bifurcated and curved upwards. Knob of pronotum broad and high. The anterior half of the knob with carina on the sides. Apex rounded, slightly emarginated and has carinae similarly. Surfaces including elytra densely punctated with circular punctae. Fine on the latter disc and stronger on the sides.

Distribution. Ecuador and Colombia^(Endrödi, 1985, Ratcliffe, 2011).

Fig. 61. *Horridocalia delislei*

Image courtesy of Kiyotami Fukinuki.

Fig. 62. *Horridocalia delislei*

Image courtesy of Kiyotami Fukinuki.

Lycomedes

Breme, 1844

L. bubeniki
L. buckleyi
L. burmeisteri
L. enigmaticus
L. hirtipes
L. ohausi
L. ramosus
L. reichei
L. salazari
L. velutipes

Lycomedes

Breme, 1844

*Lycomedes*는 열 종이 알려져 있다.

묘사. 검은색이지만, 표면이 밝은 갈색의 털로 덮여있다[Milani, 2017]. 수컷의 머리는 보통 두 갈래로 나뉘는 뿔이 있다. 전흉배판의 뿔은 위를 향해 솟아있다. 턱의 바깥쪽은 세 개의 이빨이 있다. 더듬이는 열 개의 관절이 있고, 곤봉은 짧다. Prosternal process가 짧거나 약간 길다. 앞 경절은 두껍고 세 개의 이빨이 있다. 뒷 경절은 끝으로 갈수록 넓어지며 가로지르는 용골은 없다. 앞 부절은 두껍고, 안쪽 발톱이 크게 휘었다[Endrődi, 1985].

Lycomedes is known as ten species.

Description. Black, however, covered with light brown tomentose[Milani, 2017]. Head of male usually armed with a bifurcated horn. Pronotum armed with an upward directed horn. Outer side of mandibles with three teeth. Antenna ten jointed, and club short. Prosternal process short or moderately long. Protibia strong, tridentated. Metatibia dilated to the apex, and transverse carina absent. Protarsi thickened, and inner claw strongly curved[Endrődi, 1985].

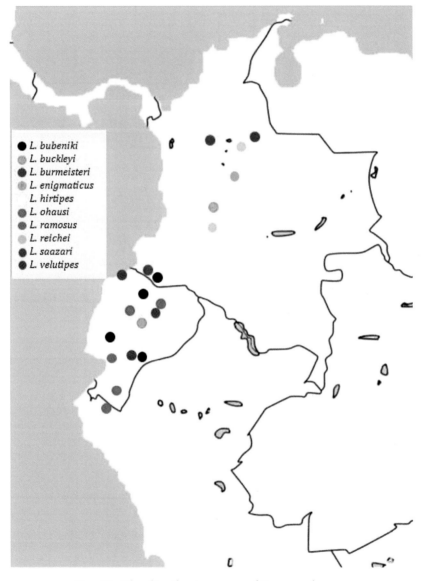

Fig. 63. The distribution map of *Lycomedes*.

*Lycomedes*의 검색표

1. – 머리뿔은 세 갈래로 나뉜다..*buckleyi*
1' – 머리뿔은 두 갈래로 나뉜다..2

buckleyi

to 2

2. – 기부에 높고 두 갈래로 나뉘는 분기점이 있다....................................*ramosus*
2' – 머리뿔은 끝에서 두 갈래로 나뉘며 기부에는 이빨이 있거나 없다................3

ramosus

3. – 기부에 이빨이 있다..*reichei*
3' – 기부에 이빨이 없다..4

reichei

4. – 머리뿔 기부의 윗면에 홈이 없다..5
4' – 머리뿔 기부의 윗면에 홈이 있고, 홈은 날카로운 용골 구조가 이룬다.........6

to 5

to 6

5. – 전흉배판의 앞면 테두리에 작은 용골구조가 있고, 대형 개체는 가슴뿔이 수직으로 높다..*enigmaticus*
5' – 전흉배판의 앞면 테두리에 작은 용골구조가 없다......................................7

6. – 다리는 강모로 덮였고, 뒷 경절은 많은 가시같은 돌기가 바깥쪽 모서리와 용골구조를 따라 나였다..*velutipes*
6' – 다리는 강모로 덮이지 않았다. 뒷 경절은 길고 거센 털이 듬성듬성 나였다.
....*hirtipes*

7. – 전흉배판이 거세고 불규칙적인 점각으로 덮여있다. 일부는 합쳐지기도 한다. 머리뿔의 기부는 넓어져 삼각형 모양의 돌기가 있다...........................*salazari*
7' – 전흉배판은 두드러지는 점각이 없다. 머리뿔의 기부가 넓어져 만들어지는 돌기는 없다..8

salazari

to 8

8. – 가슴뿔은 끝이 둥글고 양 옆은 평행하다. 전흉배판의 옆 테두리는 강하고 균일하게 앞에서 뒤로 각져 있다. 겉날개는 뒷 쪽이 약하게 넓다..............*burmeisteri*

8' – 가슴뿔의 끝은 반구형으로 확장된다. 전흉배판의 옆 테두리는 앞의 모서리 바로 뒤에서 약하게 또는 강하게 함입되며 뒷 모서리로 강하게 각진다. 겉날개는 평행하다...9

9. – 가슴뿔의 끝 부분은 구형이다. 가운데는 깊게 함입되어 양쪽 이빨이 삼각형에 가깝고, 앞으로 그리고 아래로 접힌다..............................*ohausi*

9' – 가슴뿔의 끝이 가운데에서 약하게 함입되어 구형을 만들지 않고, 앞으로 접히지 않는다...*bubeniki*

ohausi   *bubeniki*

Fig. 64. *Lycomedes* sp.

Fig. 58. Key to species of *Lycomedes*

1. – Cephalic horn trifurcated...*buckleyi*
1' – Cephalic horn bifurcated..2

buckleyi

to 2

2. – Cephalic horn, near to basis with a high bifurcated ramification...***ramosus***
2' – Cephalic horn only distally bifurcated, basally with or without a tooth....3

ramosus

3. – Cephalic horn basally with a tooth...*reichei*
3' – Cephalic horn basally without a tooth...4

reichei

4. – Cephalic horn lacking furrows on superior edge......................................5
4' – Cephalic horn with a superior edge furrowed, both furrow sides with sharp keel..6

to 5   to 6

5. – Anterior pronotal margin with a small keel, long pronotal horn erected vertically in major male..*enigmaticus*
5' – Pronotal horn short...7

6. – Legs covered with setae, metatibia with numerous short thorn-like bristles medially on the external longitudinal edge and on the oblique keels.....
....*velutipes*
6' – Legs not covered with setae, metatibia with long, coarse and scattered hairs...*hirtipes*

7. – Pronotum completely covered with coarse irregular punctures, some coalescent, cephalic horn basally widened in a triangular shaped projection.....
....*salazari*
7' – Pronotum with fine scattered punctures, cephalic horn lacking basal subtriangular laminar projections..8

salazari   to 8

8. – Pronotal horn with apex rounded and sides parallel, Pronotal lateral margins strongly, evenly arcuate from anterior to posterior angles, Elytra weakly, posteriorly dilated..*burmeisteri*
8' – Pronotal horn with apex of major males hemispherically dilated, Pronotal lateral margins weakly to strongly invaginated just behind anterior angle and then strongly arcuate to posterior angles, Elytra subparallel............................9

9. – Apex of pronotal horn bulbous, deeply emarginated in center, each side tooth broadly subtrianglular, folding forward and downward................*ohausi*
9' – Apex of pronotal horn weakly incised at center, not forming 2 broadly subtriangular teeth, not folding forward...*bubeniki*

ohausi

bubeniki

Fig. 65. *Lycomedes ramosus*

Lycomedes bubeniki

Milani, 2017

묘사. 가슴 뿔의 끝 부분과 가장자리를 제외하고 밝은 갈색의 얇은 털이 가득하다. 가슴 뿔은 헤이즐넛 색이다. 머리는 검은색이고, 미세한 주름이 있다. 이마방패의 끝 부분은 머리 뿔의 기부로 일부분 덮여있다. 턱은 세 개의 이빨이 뚜렷하다. 머리뿔은 크고 뒤로 휘었다. 기부는 삼각형이고, 두 갈래로 갈라지는 부위의 단면은 앞뒤로 평평해 거의 타원형이다. 가슴뿔은 두드러지고 위를 향해 약간 앞으로 휜 꼭짓점을 가진다. 꼭짓점에서 중심으로 약간 홈이 파여 있어 두 개의 반구를 만든다. 앞 경절은 세 개의 이빨을 가지고 가운데 이빨이 조금 더 길다[Milani, 2017].

분포. 에콰도르에 서식한다[Milani, 2017].

Description. Light brown tomentose cover the surface except the apex of thoracic horn and the margins. Thoracic horn hazelnut color. Head black, and dorsally finely rugose. Apex of clypeus covered by the base of the cephalic horn. Mandible with strong three teeth. Cephalic horn massive and curved backwards. The basal section is triangular, and the section of the close part to the bifurcation flattened and nearly elliptical. Thoracic horn prominent and projects upwards with a slight anterior inclination to the vertex. The vertex of thoracic horn faintly incised at the center, thus forming two small hemispherical subunits. Protibia tridentated. Middle one slightly longer than the others[Milani, 2017].

Distribution. Ecuador[Milani, 2017].

Remark

*L. bubeniki*는 *L. ohausi*로 오동정된 상태로 유통되는 경우가 대부분이다.
Most of *L. bubeniki* is sold as the name of *L. ohausi*.

Fig. 66. Aedeagus of *L. bubeniki*

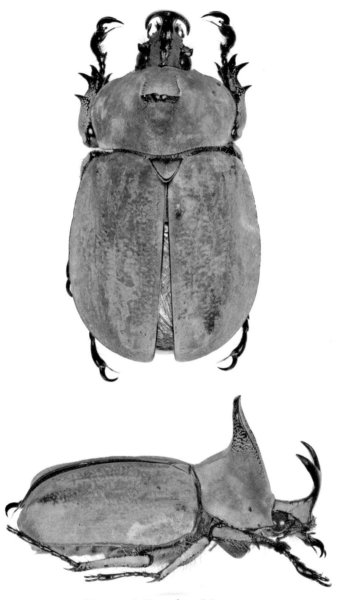

Cotopaxi, Ecuador, 34 mm
Fig. 67. *Lycomedes bubeniki*

Lycomedes buckleyi

Waterhouse, 1880

묘사. 머리의 뿔이 세 갈래로 갈라진다. 양 옆에 두 개의 이빨이 있고, 그 뒤로 하나가 갈라진다. 머리가 전부 뿔의 기부로 가려진다. 전흉배판의 뿔은 평평하고 양 옆이 평행하다. 끝은 볼록하게 굽고, 끝 부분의 중앙은 조금 톱니모양으로 오목하다. 전흉배판은 크고 좁은 원형 점각으로 덮여 있다. 항문상판은 짧고 조금 볼록하다. 앞 경절의 가장 아래 이빨은 가장 끝 부분의 이빨과 분명하게 떨어져있다. 앞 부절은 두껍다. 생식기는 짧고, 바깥 부분이 단순하게 휘었다[Endrōdi, 1985].

분포. 에콰도르에 서식한다[Endrōdi, 1985].

Description. Horn of head trifurcated. Behind the lateral two teeth, the third one is projected. Entire head covered by basis of horn. Pronotal horn flat, sides parallel. Apex curved convexly, and middle emarginated. Pronotum covered with big, shallow, and circular punctures. Pygidium short and moderately convex. Basal tooth of protibia distinctly separated to the apical tooth. Protarsi thickened. Paramere is short and sides are simply curved[Endrōdi, 1985].

Distribution. Ecuador[Endrōdi, 1985].

Fig. 68. Aedeagus of *L. buckleyi*

Napo, Ecuador, 32.5mm, 32mm

Fig. 69. *Lycomedes buckleyi*

Lycomedes burmeisteri

Waterhouse, 1879

묘사. *L. ohausi*와 유사한 종이다. 전흉배판의 뿔이 끝으로 갈수록 넓어지지 않고, 뾰족해진다. 겉날개는 뒤로 넓어진다. 이마방패는 둥글다. 머리 뿔은 뒤로 용골모양이 있고[Endrödi, 1985] 삼각형 돌기는 없다. 전흉배판은 작고 드문 점각이 있다[Neita-Moreno, 2019].

분포. 콜롬비아에 서식한다.

Description. It resembles to *L. ohausi*. Horn of the pronotum not dilated to the apex, but acuminated. Elytra dilated backwards. Clypeus rounded. Frontal horn keeled behind[Endrödi, 1985], and no triangular projection. Pronotum is covered by sparse, and small punctures[Neita-Moreno, 2019].

Distribution. Colombia.

Remark

*L. ohausi, L. burmeisteri, L. bubeniki*의 소형 개체는 서로 구분하기 어렵다. *L. burmeisteri*는 매우 제한적인 서식지에서만 서식하거나 자연에서 멸종되었을지 모른다[Pardo-Locarno, 2020]

Minor males of *L. ohausi, L. burmeisteri, L. bubeniki* are nearly indistinguishable. It is assumed that *L. burmeisteri* has been extincted or distributed in very limited area[Pardo-Locarno, 2020].

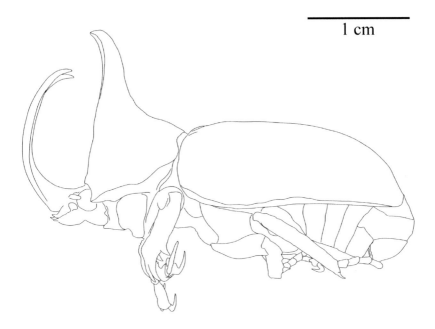

Fig. 70. *Lycomedes burmeisteri*

Lycomedes enigmaticus
Neita-Moreno & Ratcliffe, 2019

묘사. *L. hirtipes*와 유사한 종이다. 하지만 다음과 같은 차이점이 있다. 이마방패의 끝 부분이 측면으로 살짝 돌출된다. 이마는 뿔 뒤에 긴 홈 혹은 좁은 선이 있다. *L. hirtipes*에게는 홈이 삼각형 모양이다. 전흉배판의 앞쪽 경계에 작은 용골이 있다. Prosternal process는 포물선 모양이다. *L. hirtipes*의 경우 둥글다. 생식기의 끝 부분에는 강모가 없다[Neita-Moreno, 2019]. 대형 개체의 경우, 머리뿔의 앞 부분의 기부는 두드러진 홈이 있으며, 그 홈은 용골 모양에 의해 끊긴다. 이 용골 모양은 머리의 앞 부분에서 시작된다. 전흉에는 높게 솟은 뿔이 있으며 끝 부분은 직각으로 굽어 넓어진다.

분포. 콜롬비아의 톨리마에 서식한다[Neita-Moreno, 2019].

Description. It resembles to *L. hirtipes*. However, it differs by following characters. Each side of the clypeal apex is projecting slightly laterad. Frons has elongated groove or a narrow line behind the horn. In *L. hirtipes*, the groove is subtriangular. The anterior pronotal margin has a small keel. The prosternal process is slightly parabolic. In *L. hirtipes*, it is rounded. The setae is absent at the apex if the paramere[Neita-Moreno, 2019]. In major males, posterior part of cephalic horn with prominent groove, delimited by paths of carina, which begins at frontal region of head. Pronotal horn high and widened, parabolic.

Distribution. Tolima, Colombia[Neita-Moreno, 2019].

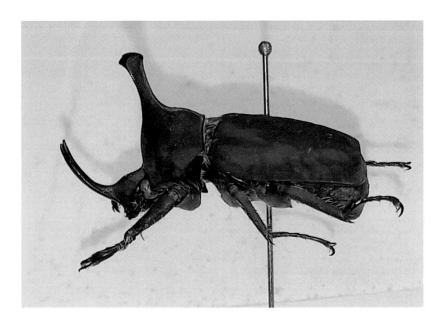

Image courtesy of Luis Carlos Pardo-Locarno.

Fig. 71. *Lycomedes enigmaticus*

Lycomedes hirtipes

Arrow, 1902

묘사. 다리에 드물고 길며 두꺼운 털이 있다. 이마방패는 조금 길며 끝부분이 잘린듯한 모양이다. 전흉배판의 뿔은 짧고 위를 향한다. 항문상판은 조금 길고 강하게 볼록하다. 앞 경절의 가장 아래 이빨은 가장 위 이빨과 멀리 떨어져 있다. 앞 부절은 두껍다. 생식기는 길고 얇으며, 바깥쪽이 조금 넓다(Endrödi, 1985).

분포. 콜롬비아에 서식한다(Endrödi, 1985).

Description. Sparse, long, and thick setae are on the leg. Clypeus moderately long and truncated. Pronotal horn short and directed upwards. Pygidium moderately long and strongly convex. Basal tooth of protibia far from apical tooth. Protarsi thickened. Paramere long, slender, and the outer sides are dilated in the middle(Endrödi, 1985).

Distribution. Colombia(Endrödi, 1985).

Fig. 72. Aedeagus of *L. hirtipes*

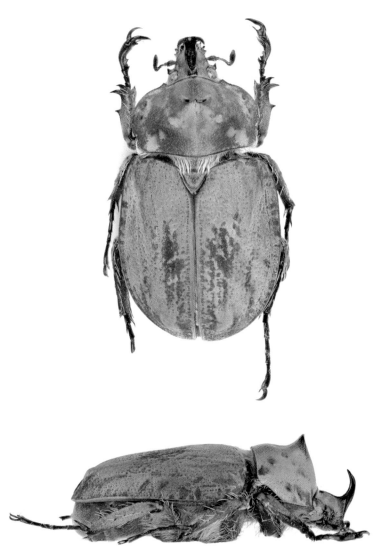

Colombia, 32 mm

Fig. 73. *Lycomedes hirtipes*

Lycomedes ohausi
Arrow, 1908

묘사. 대형 수컷의 가슴뿔은 끝 부분이 반구형으로 넓어진다. 소형 개체에서는 두드러지지 않는다. 겉날개는 거의 넓어지지 않는다. 가운데에서 가장 넓다. 이마방패의 끝 부분은 잘린듯한 모양이고, 양 옆의 모서리가 뾰족하며 두드러지게 튀어나온다. 겉날개의 봉합선과 어깨 뒤에서만 강한 점각을 볼 수 있다. 앞 부절이 두껍다[Endrödi, 1985,].

분포. 에콰도르와 페루에 서식한다[Milani, 2017].

Description. Apex of pronotal horn of big male hemispherically dilated. In small males, less distinct. Elytra not or scarcely dilated backwards, broadest in the middle. Apex of clypeus truncated, and lateral angles sharp and prolonged. Strong punctures only at the suture of elytra and behind of shoulders. Protarsi thickened[Endrödi, 1985,].

Distribution. Ecuador and Peru[Milani, 2017].

Remark

에콰도르 전역에 서식한다고 믿어졌던 이 종은 Milani에 의해 *L. bubeniki*가 분리되면서 에콰도르와 페루 접경지역에서 서식하는 개체군으로 좁혀졌다. 그러나 이후 Ratcliffe의 조사 결과, 에콰도르에서도 넓게 분포하는 것으로 밝혀졌다.

This species is considered to inhabit in broad area of Ecuador. However, *L. bubeniki* is separated by Milani, the habitats of this species are narrowed down to the border of Peru-Ecuador. However, after the investigation by Ratcliffe, it is also distributed in wide area of Ecuador.

Loja, Ecuador, 36 mm

Fig. 74. *Lycomedes ohausi*

Lycomedes ohausi
@Eunjoong Kim

Lycomedes ramosus

Arrow, 1902

묘사. 머리의 뿔은 기부에 두 갈래로 갈라지는 분지가 있다. 가슴뿔은 짧다. 이마방패는 둥글다. 항문상판은 강하게 볼록하고, 끝 부분이 배 아래로 후퇴해있다. 앞 부절이 강하게 두껍다[Endrödi, 1985]. Arrow가 종으로 발표할 당시 오직 하나의 표본만이 존재했다. Arrow는 해당 종을 이렇게 묘사했다. "회색-올리브색, 불명확한 갈색, 매끄러움, 안각은 급하게 발달함, ... 이 종은 두 갈래로 훌륭히 갈라지는 머리 뿔으로나, 뚜렷한 대리석 무늬로 보나, *Lycomedes*중 최고의 종이다."[Arrow, 1902].

분포. 콜롬비아에 서식한다.

Description. Horn of head bifurcated near to the base. Pronotal horn short. Clypeus is rounded. Pygidium strongly convex, and apex is retracted under the abdomen. Protarsi strongly thickened[Endrödi, 1985]. When Arrow described L.ramosus for the first time, he depicted it: "grayish-olivaceous, nebulosus brown, velvet, ocular canthus developed acute, ... This is the finest of its genus, both from the great development of its doubly-branched cephalic horn and the conspicuous marbling of its upper surface."[Arrow, 1902].

Distribution. Colombia.

A single male specimen was included in the collection bequeathed to the Museum by the late Philip Crowley, and is the only representative of the species at present known. It is the finest of its genus, both from the great development of its doubly-branched cephalic horn and the conspicuous marbling of its upper surface. The prosternum is raised into a basin-shaped structure behind the coxæ.

Fig. 75. The original description of *L. ramosus*.

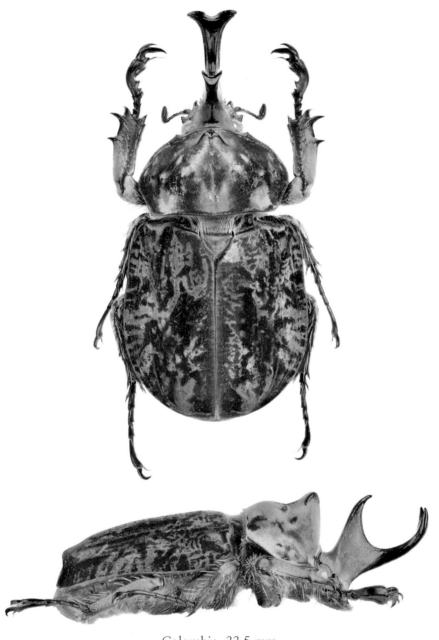

Colombia, 33.5 mm

Fig. 76. *Lycomedes ramosus*

Lycomedes reichei

Brème, 1844

묘사. 머리뿔의 기부에 이빨이 있다. 표면은 회색-갈색이다. 항문상판에 매우 짧은 털이 있다. 이마방패는 넓게 잘린듯한 모양이다. 가슴뿔은 좁고 평평하며, 가운데를 따라 홈이 있고, 끝 부분이 잘린듯한 모양이다. 겉날개에는 뚜렷한 점각이 있다. 앞 부절이 두껍다[Endrödi, 1985].

분포. 콜롬비아의 산탄데르에 서식한다.

Description. A tooth on the hind edge of the frontal horn, near the base. Pygidium with very short bristles. Clypeus broadly truncated. Pronotal horn narrow and flat, furrowed along the middle, apex truncated. Elytra with distinct punctures. Protarsi thickened[Endrödi, 1985].

Distribution. Santander, Colombia.

Genus LYCOMEDES.

Cephalic horn toothed at base:
  basal tooth large, bifid . . . . *ramosus*, sp. n.
  basal tooth small . . . . *Reichei*, De Brême.
Cephalic horn bilaminate at base:
  legs velvety . . . . *velutipes*, sp. n.
  legs pilose . . . . *hirtipes*, sp. n.
Cephalic horn unarmed at base:
  bifid at apex . . . . *Burmeisteri*, Waterh.
  trifid at apex . . . . *Buckleyi*, Waterh.

Identification key of Lycomedes by Arrow, 1902.

Remark

L. lydiae가 이 종의 동물이명이라는 주장이 있으나, Pardo-Locarno 는 2020년 그의 글에서 L. lydiae가 여전히 분리된 종임을 주장했다[Pardo-Locarno, 2020]. 해당 논문에서 제시한 L. reichei의 사진은 L. lydiae의 묘사와 일치하는 등, 논란이 있다.

L. lydiae was synonymized with L. reichei in 2019 by Ratcliffe, but Pardo-Locarno argued that they are still two distinct species[Pardo-Locarno, 2020]. It is controversial for some reasons. Image of L. reichei that provided in the article fits in the description of L. lydiae.

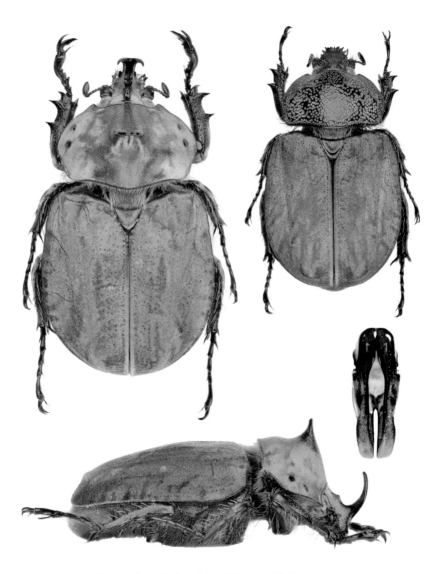

Santander, Colombia, 26 mm, 24.5 mm

Fig. 77. *Lycomedes reichei*

Lycomedes salazari

Pardo-Locarno, Villalabos-Moreno & Stechauner, 2015

묘사. 머리뿔의 끝부분이 두갈래로 나뉜다. 뿔의 기부에는 어떠한 돌출도 없다. 이러한 점에서 *L. ohausi, L. burmeisteri*와 유사하지만 전흉배판이 크고 불규칙적인, 일부는 합쳐지기도 하는 점각으로 덮인 점이 다르다. 머리뿔의 기부는 양 옆으로 넓다. 안쪽 발톱이 삼각형 모양의 돌기를 가지고 있다는 점에서 모든 다른 종과 구분된다[Pardo-Locarno, 2015].

분포. 콜롬비아의 산탄데르에 서식한다[Pardo-Locarno, 2015].

Description. Cephalic horn bifurcated. No projection at the base of cephalic horn. In this aspect it resembles *L. ohausi* and *L. burmeisteri*, but it differs by the pronotum covered with thick irregular punctures, some coalescing. Base of cephalic horn basally wide. Inner claw with triangular projection, which differs from all other species of its genus[Pardo-Locarno, 2015].

Distribution. Santander, Colombia[Pardo-Locarno, 2015].

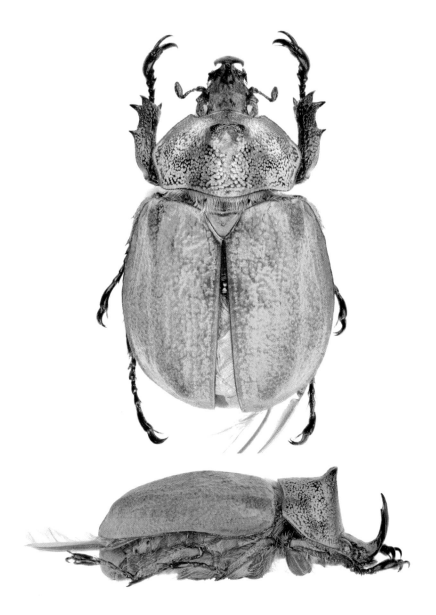

Santander, Colombia, 28 mm

Fig. 78. *Lycomedes salazari*

Lycomedes velutipes
Arrow, 1902

묘사. 다리에 몇 개의 긴 강모가 있고, 갈색 털이 밀생해있다. 머리의 뿔은 기부로 향할수록 둔하게 넓어진다. 뿔은 다른 종 보다 조금 더 앞을 향한다. 전흉배판에는 점각이 보이지 않지만, 겉날개에는 점열이 선명하다.

분포. 에콰도르에 서식한다[Endrödi, 1985].

Description. Few fine, long setae and brown tomentose on the legs. Cephalic horn obtusely dilated on the basis. Both horns directed more forward than the other species. Pronotum has no visible punctures, but rows of punctures distinct on elytra.

Distribution. Ecuador[Endrödi, 1985].

Fig. 79. Aedeagus of *L. velutipes*

Esmeraldas, Ecuador, 30 mm

Fig. 80. *Lycomedes velutipes*

Minisiderus

Endrödi, 1970

M. benjamini
M. bertolossiorum
M. elyanae
M. goyanus
M. martinae
M. matogrossensis
M. minicola
M. mielkeorum
M. paranensis
   paranensis
   lenorae

Minisiderus

Endrödi, 1970

*Minisiderus*는 9개 종과 2개 아종으로 이루어져 있다.

묘사. 금속 광택이 없는 갈색이다. 머리에는 긴 두 갈래로 갈라지는 뿔이 있다. 턱은 이마방패로 덮인다. 더듬이는 10마디로 이루어져 있고 곤봉마디는 짧다. 전흉배판은 볼록하거나 끝 부분 뒤에 두 개의 결절이 있다. 겉날개에는 봉합선이 있고 불규칙적으로 점각이 있다. 전미절에는 소리를 내는 기관이 없다. 앞 경절은 세 개 혹은 네 개의 이빨이 있다[Endrödi, 1985].

Minisiderus is known as nine species and two subspecies.

Description. Brown without metallic lustre. Head of male with two small triangular horns. Mandibles covered by the clypeus. Antenna ten jointed and club short. Pronotum convex or with two tubercles behind the apical margin. Elytra with sutural stria and irregular punctae. Propygidium without stridulatory area. Protibia with three or four teeth[Endrödi, 1985].

Fig. 81. The distribution map of *Minisiderus*.

*Minisiderus*의 검색표

1.- 전흉배판 앞면에 뿔이 세워져있다...*matogrossensis*
1'- 전흉배판 앞면에 뿔이 세워져있지 않다..2

matogrossensis

2.- 머리뿔은 연결되어 머리보다 훨씬 좁다. 이마는 부드럽고 전미절에 강모가
없다...*paranensis*
2'- 머리뿔이 연결된 기부가 머리의 반 이상으로 넓다. 이마는 점각이 있고 전미
절에 작은 강모가 있다.,...3

 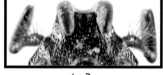

paranensis   **to 3**

3.- 머리뿔의 양 옆에 돌기가 있다...............................*bertolossiorum*
3'- 머리뿔의 양 옆에 돌기가 없다...4

bertolossiorum

4.- 머리뿔은 뿔의 길이보다 짧은 거리로 연결되어 있다....................8
4'- 머리뿔은 뿔의 길이 이상의 거리로 연결되어 있다.....................5

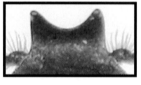

5   **8**

5.- 이마에 돌기가 있다...*mielkeorum*
5'- 이마에 돌기가 없다...6

mielkorum

6.- 더듬이 곤봉이 이마보다 길다. 20 mm 이하의 작은 크기다.............*martinae*
6'- 더듬이 곤봉이 이마보다 짧다..7

martinae

7.- 겉날개에 주름이 있고 바이올렛 색이다.......................................*benjamini*
7'- 겉날개는 주름이나 바이올렛 색이 없다..*goyanus*

benjamini

goyanus

8.- 이마는 납작하지 않다... *elyanae*
8'- 이마는 강하게 납작하다..*minicola*

elyanae

minicola

Key to species of *Minisiderus*

1.- Erected horn on anterior pronotum border.......................*matogrossensis*
1'- No erected horn on anterior pronotum border..2

matogrossensis

2.- Conjoint frontal horn basis much narrower than head, frons smooth. Pygidium without setae..*paranensis*
2'- Conjoint frontal horn basis wider than half of head, frons punctate. Pygidium with many small setae 3

paranensis   **to 3**

3.- Frontal horns with lateral spiniform process ....*bertolossiorum*
3'- Frontal horns without lateral spiniform process 4

bertolossiorum

4.- Frontal horns not separated from each other more than the width of a horn..8
4'- Frontal horns separated from each other more than the width of a horn..
....5

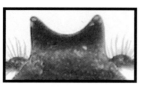 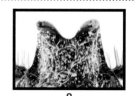

5   **8**

5.- Frons with transverse process ....*mielkeorum*
5'- Frons simple, without transverse process 6

mielkorum

6.- Antennal club much larger than frons, small sized, under 20 mm.............
....*martinae*
6'- Antennal club shorter than frons..7

martinae

7.- Elytra with transverse rugae and violaceus shine........................*benjamini*
7'- Elytra punctated, without rugae or violaceus shine......................*goyanus*

benjamini   *goyanus*

8.- Frons not depressed.. *elyanae*
8'- Frons strongly depressed..*minicola*

elyanae   *minicola*

Minisiderus benjamini

Abadie, 2014

묘사. 몸은 긴 타원형 모양이며 볼록하다. 전흉배판은 자색으로 빛난다. 이마는 주름지고점각이 있다. 안각은 날카롭고, 이마 뿔은 넓은 기부로 연결되어 위로 강하게 휜다. 겉날개는 규칙적인 점각이 있고, 앞 쪽 봉합선 근처에 주름이 있다. 항문상판은 양 옆이 주름져있고, 디스크에는 점각이 있다. 앞 경절은 세 개의 이빨이 있다. 생식기는 둥글고 양 옆으로 매우 확장되어 있다[(Abadie, 2014)].

진단. 이 종은 생식기의 모양과 넓은 기부로 분리되는 이마의 뿔, 빛나는 자색으로 구분된다. 이마뿔이 *M. mielkeorum*과 유사하지만 조금 덜 분리되어 있고 상승하는 각도로 돌출된 부위가 없다는 점에서 구분된다[(Abadie, 2014)].

분포. 브라질의 마토 그로소에 서식한다[(Abadie, 2014)].

Description. The body is elongated oval shape and convex. The pronotum is violaceus and shining. The fron is rugose and punctated. The eye canthus is sharp, the frontal horns are connected with wide base and strongly curved upwards. The elytra have regular punctates, and close to the anterior suture some wrinkles are present. The pygidium is rugose on the sides, and punctures are on the disc. The protibia have three teeth. The paramere is rounded and laterally expanded[(Abadie, 2014)].

Diagnosis. This species can be distinguished by the shape of the paramere, violaceus shining, the frontal horns separated by wide base. The frontal horns resemble *M. mielkeorum*, but it differs by slightly minor separation of horns and lack of the elevated angled process[(Abadie, 2014)].

Distribution. Mato Grosso, Brazil[(Abadie, 2014)].

Fig. 82. *Minisiderus benjamini*

Holotype
Image courtesy of Pablo Wagner
and Esteban Abadie.

Minisiderus bertolossiorum

Abadie, Koike & Godinho 2016

묘사. 몸은 긴 타원형 모양이며 볼록하다. 이마방패는 짧고 오목하며, 드물게 점각이 있다. 이마는 눌려있고 드물게 점각이 있다. 안각은 기부에서 뾰족하며 작고 많은 털이 있다. 두 개의 짧은 기부로 연결되고 위로 향하며 양 옆에 돌출된 부위가 있는 이마 뿔이 있다. 전흉배판은 불규칙한 점각이 있고 앞쪽은 조금 솟아오르며 두 개의 평평한 결절이 있다. 경절은 세 개의 이빨을 가진다. 더듬이는 10개의 관절로 이루어지고, 곤봉은 나머지 10개의 관절과 같은 길이이다. 겉 날개는 약한 점각이 있고, 점열이 일부 존재한다. 항문 상판은 양 옆이 주름져있고, 디스크에는 약한 점각이 있으며 드물게 노란 털이 있다. 생식기는 짧고 끝 부분이 좁다[Abadie, 2016].

분포. 브라질의 고이아스에 서식한다[Abadie, 2016].

Description. Body elongated oval shape. Clypeus short and concave with sparse punctures. Frons depressed and sparsely punctated. Ocular canthus acute at the base and with many small setae. Frontal horns short, connected with short base, curved upwards and laterally projected process. Pronotum irregularly punctated. At the anterior border, two tubercles elevated and flattened. Protibia with three theeth. Antenna ten jointed and the club as long as all other joints. Elytra weakly punctated and with some rows of punctures. Pygidium rugose at the sides and weakly punctated on the disc, with sparse yellowish setae. Paramere short and narrow at the apex[Abadie, 2016].

Distribution. Goias, Brazil[Abadie, 2016].

Fig. 83. *Minisiderus bertolossiorum* Holotype

Image courtesy of Pablo Wagner
and Esteban Abadie.

Minisiderus elyanae

Dechambre, 2009

묘사. 몸은 긴 타원형이며 빛나는 붉은 갈색이다. 이마방패는 짧고 둥글며 강한 점각이 조금 있다. 안각은 두드러지지 않고 둥글다. 이마는 평평하거나 아주 살짝 눌린 모양이며, 점각과 주름이 많다. 강하게 휜 뿔은 뒤를 향한다. 전흉배판은 넓고 앞 쪽 경계 뒤에, 경계와는 분리된 두 개의 돌기가 있다. 강하고, 드문 점각이 있다. 전미절에는 소리를 내는 기관이 없고, 미세한 노란 털로 덮여있다. 앞 경절은 세 개의 이빨이 있다. 앞 부절은 얇고, 발톱의 크기는 같다[(Dechambre, 2009)].

분포. 브라질의 마라냥에 서식한다[(Dechambre, 2009)].

Description. Body robust and elongated oval shape. Reddish brown and glabrous. Clypeus short, broadly rounded, and strongly and less densely punctated. Ocular canthus not prominent, rounded. Frons flat or slightly depressed. Densely punctated and wrinkled. Frontal horn strongly curved backwards. Pronotum broad, and behind the anterior margin, double tubercles situated, but separated from the margin. Also, strongly, and sparsely punctated. Propygidium without stridulatory area, covered with fine yellow hairs. Protibia tridentated. Protarsi fine. Claws equal[(Dechambre, 2009)].

Distribution. Maranhao, Brazil[(Dechambre, 2009)].

Maranhao, Brazil, 26 mm

Fig. 84. *Minisiderus elyanae*

Minisiderus goyanus
Ohaus, 1930

묘사. 앞 경절의 4개 이빨이 서로 같은 간격으로 떨어져 있다. 기부의 이빨은 작고 뾰족하다. 전흉배판의 끝 부분 가장자리 뒤에는 두 개의 작은 돌기가 있다. 그 뒤에 오목한 부분은 없다[Endrödi, 1985].

진단. *M. minicola*와 매우 유사하지만 생식기가 매우 다르다. 생식기는 넓고, 비대칭적이며, 끝 부분의 바깥쪽에 이빨이 있다[Endrödi, 1985]. Ohaus는 *M. minicola*보다 조금 더 크고 상대적으로 납작한 종으로 묘사하였다[Ohaus, 1930].

분포. 브라질의 고이아스에 서식한다[Abadie, 2008]

Description. Four teeth of protibia placed at equal distances. Basal tooth small and pointed. Behind the apical margin of pronotum, two tubercles are present. No pit behind tubercles[Endrödi, 1985].

Diagnosis. It is very similar to *M. minicola* but the shape of the paramere is distinct. It is very broad, asymmetrical and tooth is present on the outer side of the apex[Endrödi, 1985]. Ohaus depicted *M. goyanus* as slightly larger and relatively flatter than *M. minicola*[Ohaus, 1930].

Distribution. Goias, Brazil[Abadie, 2008].

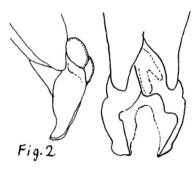

Fig. 85. The paramere of *M. goyanus* (Ohaus, 1930)

Mato Grosso, Brazil, 26.5 mm

Fig. 86. *Minisiderus goyanus*

Minisiderus martinae

Abadie, 2010

묘사. 몸은 길지만 *Minisiderus*의 다른 종들 보다는 짧다. 이마방패는 짧고, 그 길이가 넓이와 같다. 드물게 점각이 있고 가운데가 강하게 오목하다. 안각은 기부가 둔하다. 이마의 뿔은 위를 향하고, 단면이 삼각형이며, 뿔의 크기만큼 서로 떨어져 있다. 더듬이의 곤봉은 모든 관절을 합한 것보다 길다. 전흉배판의 앞쪽은 두 개의 평평하고 둥근, 앞을 향하는 돌기가 있다. 반면, *M. matogrossensis*는 위를 향한다. 겉날개는 점열이 있고, 각 점각 사이의 거리는 점각보다 크다. 항문상판의 옆은 주름지고, 디스크는 약한 점각이 있다. 앞 경절은 네 개의 이빨이 있고 가장 기부의 것은 작다. 생식기는 둥글고 짧으며, 끝 부분이 매우 짧다[(Abadie, 2010)].

분포. 볼리비아의 치퀴토스에 서식한다[(Abadie, 2010)].

Description. Body elongated but shorter than other species of *Minisiderus*. Clypeus short and as long as broad, ssparsely punctuated and strongly concave at the middle. Ocular canthus basally obtuse. Frontal horn curved upwards, triangular in cross section and separated by the size of the horn. Club of antenna longer than all joints. Anterior part of pronotum with two tubercles that is flattened and rounded, directed forward. However, tubercles of *M. matogrossensis* upwards. Elytra with rows of punctures. The distance between two punctures is longer than the puncture. Sides of pygidium rugose and the disc weakly punctated. Protibia with four teeth and basal one small. Paramere rounded, short, and apical region very short[(Abadie, 2010)].

Distribution. Chiquitos, Bolivia[(Abadie, 2010)].

Santa Cruz, Bolivia, 18 mm

Fig. 87. *Minisiderus martinae*

Minisiderus matogrossensis

Ohaus, 1930

묘사. 앞 경절에 있는 네 개의 이빨이 서로 다른 거리로 떨어져있다. 위의 두 개와 아래의 두 개는 멀리 떨어져 있다. 전흉배판에는 바로 서있는 작은 뿔이 끝 부분 가장자리의 중간에 있다. 그 뒤는 오목하다. 암컷에게도 두 뿔의 흔적을 볼 수 있으며, 오목한 부분은 없다. 겉날개는 미세하게 그물모양이고 불규칙적인 점각이 있다. 항문상판은 부드럽고 빛난다. 생식기는 약하게 비대칭적이다. 바깥쪽은 둥글고 끝 부분은 뾰족하다(Endrödi, 1985).

분포. 브라질의 마토 그로소에 서식한다(Ohaus, 1930).

Description. Four teeth of protibiae placed at unequal distances. Each pairs of two apical and two basal teeth are far from each other. Pronotum with erected small horn at the middle of the apical margin, pit behind the horn. In females, with two traces of tubercles, without a pit. Elytra finely reticulated and irregularly punctated. Pygidium smooth and shining. Paramere weakly asymmetric, outer sides rounded and the apex sharp(Endrödi, 1985).

Distribution. Mato Grosso, Brazil(Ohaus, 1930).

Mato Grosso, Brazil, 21 mm

Fig. 88. *Minisiderus matogrossensis*

Minisiderus mielkeorum

Grossi & Grossi, 2005

묘사. 몸은 길고 달걀모양이다. 붉거나 어두운 갈색이며, 등은 빛나고 부드럽다. 이마방패는 짧고 머리의 반 정도 넓이를 가진다. 뿔은 위로 강하게 휘었고, 단면이 삼각형이다. 기부에서 두 뿔은 멀리 떨어져있다. 이마를 가로지르는 각진 돌기가 있다. 안각의 점각은 서로 합쳐진다. 안각의 기부는 둔각이고 드물게 작은 강모가 있다. 전흉배판은 모든 가장자리에 경계가 있다. 매우 볼록하며 양 옆으로 둥글다. 밀도있는 점각이 있으며 디스크에서는 점각이 합쳐지기도 한다. 겉날개는 불규칙적인 점각으로 가득하다. 어깨 부위에서는 점각이 더 작아진다. 항문상판은 매우 작은 강모로 주름져있다. 앞 경절은 세 개의 이빨이 있다[Grossi, 2005].

진단. 이 종은 이마의 가로지르는 각진 돌기와 안각의 모양으로 다른 종과 구분된다[Grossi, 2005].

분포. 브라질의 마라냥에 서식한다[Grossi, 2005].

Description. Body elongated and oval shape. Reddish to dark brown, and dorsally glabrous and smooth. Clypeus short, as wide as the half of the head. Horns strongly angled upwards, and the cross-section triangular. Horns very separated at the base. Transversal process which is elevated and angled on the frons. Base of ocular canthus obtuse with sparse small setae. Pronotum bordered all around, and very convex, laterally rounded, densely punctated and coalescent on the disc. Elytra covered with irregular punctures. Humeral punctures are smaller. Pygidium rugulose with very small setae. Protibia with three teeth[Grossi, 2005].

Diagnosis. This species differs from all other species by the transversal angled process on the frons and the shape of the ocular canthus[Grossi, 2005].

Distribution. Maranhao, Brazil[Grossi, 2005].

Maranhao, Brazil, 24 mm
Fig. 89. *Minisiderus mielkeorum*

Minisiderus minicola

Ohaus, 1930

묘사. 앞 경절은 세 개의 이빨이 있다. 드물게 기부가 넓어진 모습이 보이기도 한다. 이마는 드물게, 항문상판에는 짧고 밀도있게, 가슴판에는 좀 더 길고 밀도있게 강모가 있다. 이마는 깊게 두 갈래로 갈라진, 똑바로 선 판을 가진다. 전흉배판에는 평평한 돌기 두 개가 있다. 겉날개는 점각이 밀도있고 끝 부분에서 더 미세하다. 항문상판은 볼록하다. 생식기는 짧고 강하게 굽었다[Endrödi, 1985].

분포. 브라질의 미나스 제라이스, 마토 그로소에 서식한다[Endrödi, 1985].

Description. Protibia with three teeth. Rarely, a basal dilation is observed. At frons with sparse, at pygidium with short and dense, at sternum with rather long and dense setae. Frons with deeply bifurcated and erected plate. Pronotum with two flattened tubercles. Elytra covered with dense punctures. Punctures much finer on the sides and the apex. Pygidium convex. Paramere short and strongly curved[Endrödi, 1985].

Distribution. Minas Gerais, Mato Grosso, Brazil[Endrödi, 1985].

Fig. 90. Aedeagus of *M. minicola*

Goias, Brazil, 24 mm

Fig. 91. *Minisiderus minicola*

Minisiderus paranensis

M. p. paranensis Arrow, 1902

묘사. *Minisiderus* 중 비교적 큰 종이다. 이마의 뿔이 짧고 깊게 반으로 갈라진다. 대형 수컷의 경우 갈라져 나온 뿔의 길이가 그 줄기 부분만큼 길다. 전흉배판에는 두 결절이 있다. 앞 경절은 세 개의 이빨이 있다. 표면과 항문상판에는 강모가 없다. 가슴판에는 비교적 긴 강모가 밀도있다. 겉 날개의 디스크는 강한 점각이 많지만 옆 부분은 작아진다. 생식기의 기부는 약하게 비대칭이고, 좁으며, 약하게 안쪽으로 휘었다[Endrödi, 1985].

분포. 브라질의 파라냐에 서식한다[Endrödi, 1985].

Description. It is relatively big species in *Minisiderus*. The frontal horn is short and deeply bifurcated. In major males, both branches are as long as its stem. The pronotum has two tubercles. There are no setae on the surface and pygidium. However, in the sternum, rather long and dense setae are present. The disc of elytra is densely and strongly punctated, and punctures are smaller on the sides. The paramere is weakly asymmetrical on the basis, narrow and weakly curved inward[Endrödi, 1985].

Distribution. Parana, Brazil.

M. p. lenorae Grossi, Dechambre & Grossi, 2014

묘사. 원명아종은 전흉배판에 두 개의 결절이 있는 반면, *M. paranensis lenorae*는 하나의 결절이 있다. 안각이 각지기 보다 둥글다[Grossi, 2012].

분포. 브라질의 브라질리아에 서식한다.

Description. *M. paranensis paranensis* has two tubercles on the pronotum, while *M. paranensis lenorae* has one tubercle. The ocular canthus is rounded rather angled[Grossi, 2012].

Distribution. Brasilia, Brazil.

Brazil, 29 mm

Fig. 92. *M. paranensis paranensis*

Brazil, 27 mm

Fig. 93. *M. paranensis lenorae*

Mitracephala

Thomson, 1859

M. humboldti
M. lachaumei

Mitracephala

Thomson, 1859

*Mitracephala*는 두 종이 알려져 있다.

묘사. 턱의 바깥쪽에 큰 두 개의 이빨이 있지만, 보통 이마방패에 가려져 있다. 더듬이는 10개의 관절을 가진다. 곤봉은 짧다. 수컷의 머리와 전흉배판에 뿔이 있지만 암컷은 없다. 겉날개는 불규칙적으로 점각이 있고, 두 날개가 만나는 선에 점열이 있다. 앞의 경절은 세 개의 이빨이 있고, 뒤의 경절은 끝으로 갈수록 두꺼워진다. 끝 부분의 테두리는 삼각형모양이다[(Endrődi, 1985)].

Mitracephala is known as two species.

Description. The outer sides of mandibles has two teeth, which normally are covered by clypeus. The antennae has 10 joints. The club is short. Males have a horn at the head and the pronotum, females are unarmed. The elytra has irregular punctures and a row of punctures is on the suture. The protibiae have three teeth and the apex of metatibiae are dilated. The apical margin of the metatibiae produced triangulary[(Endrődi, 1985)].

Fig. 94. The distribution map of *Mitracephala*.

Mitracephala humboldti

Thomson, 1859

묘사. 검고 약하게 구리색의 광택이 있다. 겉날개는 갈색이고, 봉합선과 어깨부분은 검은색이다. 표면과 항문상판에는 털이 없지만 가슴판은 길고 노란 털이 있다. 이마방패는 넓게 잘린듯한 모양이고, 오목하다. 수컷의 뿔은 두껍고 짧으며 끝 부분이 삼각형 모양으로 오목하다. 전흉배판은 넓고 옆 가장자리가 크게 휘어있으며 앞 쪽에는 짧고 강한, 앞으로 뻗은 원뿔모양 뿔이 있다. 항문상판은 매우 볼록하며 배 쪽으로 후퇴되어 있다 (Endrödi, 1985).

분포. 페루, 에콰도르, 볼리비아에 서식한다(Endrödi, 1985).

Description. Black with weak bronzy sheen. Elytra brown, and suture and spot on shoulder black. Surface and pygidium bare, but sternum covered with long yellow setae. Clypeus broadly truncated and emarginated. Horn of male thick and short. Apex triangularly emarginated. Pronotum broad and side strongly curved. Behind the anterior margin, strong, short, forward-directed conical horn present. Pygidium strongly convex and retracted under the abdomen(Endrödi, 1985).

Distribution. Peru, Ecuador, Bolivia(Endrödi, 1985).

Napo, Ecuador, 42 mm, 40 mm

Fig. 95. *Mitracephala humboldti*

Mitracephala lachaumei

Dechambre, 1992

묘사. 몸은 두껍다. 몸체, 소순판, 다리 등은 매우 어두운 검은 갈색이다. 이마방패는 짧고 넓으며 앞쪽 경계가 희미하게 굽었다. 안각은 넓고 사각형이다. 머리뿔은 짧고 두껍다. 중간 부분이 거의 직각으로 휘어 뒤를 향한다. 전흉배판은 넓고 경계가 분명하다. Prosternal process는 원뿔형이다. 겉날개는 미세한 점각이 밀도있으며, 그보다 조금 더 큰 점각이 조금 있다. 이 종은 *M. humboldti*와 더 어두운 겉날개 색깔, 머리와 가슴의 형태로 구분된다. *M. humboldti*는 전흉배판에 원뿔형 돌기가 있으며 머리뿔은 조금 굽었다. 반면, *M. lachaumei*는 직각으로 휜 뿔이 전흉배판의 꼭대기를 넘는다[Dechambre, 1992].

분포. 볼리비아에 서식한다[Dechambre, 1992].

Description. Body thick. Body, scutellum, legs very dark brownish-black. Clypeus short and wide, and anterior margin faintly curved. Ocular canthus wide and rectangular. Cephalic horn short and thick. At the middle, it curves perpendicularly, thus backwards. Pronotum wide and entirely bordered. Prosternal process conical. Elytra densely, finely punctated. Fine punctures are superposed with not-dense moderate punctures. This species is distinguished by darker elytra colouring and cephalic-thoracic morphology. *M. humboldti* has a conical tubercle on pronotum, and cephalic horn is recurved. Meanwhile, cephalic horn of *M. lachaumei* curved perpendicularly, exceeds the top of the thoracic crest[Dechambre, 1992].

Distribution. Bolivia[Dechambre, 1992].

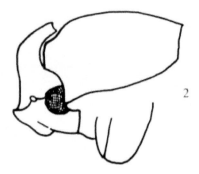

Fig. 96. *Mitracephala lachaumei*
image from Dechambre, 1992

Fig. 97. *Mitracephala humboldti*

Spodistes

Burmeister, 1847

S. angulicollis
S. armstrongi
S. batesi
S. beltianus
S. grandis
S. hopei
S. mniszechi
S. monzoni

Spodistes

Burmeister, 1847

*Spodistes*는 여덟 종으로 이루어져 있다.

묘사. 몸의 대부분은 노란 갈색의 미세한 털로 덮여있다. 수컷의 머리엔 뿔이 있고, 암컷의 경우 두 개의 강한 결절이 있다. 턱의 바깥 부분에는 세 개의 이빨이 있다. 더듬이는 10개의 마디로 이루어져 있다. Prosternal process가 없다. 전미절에는 원시적인 소리를 내는 부위가 있다. 앞 경절은 세 개의 이빨이 있고, 뒷 경절은 끝 부분으로 갈수록 넓어진다. 앞 부절은 두껍다[Endrödi, 1985].

Spodistes is known as eight species.

Description. Large part of surface covered by yellowish-brown tomentose. Head of male horned, that of females with two tubercles. Antenna ten jointed. Prosternal process absent. Propygidium with primitive stridulatory area. Protibia tridentated. Metatibia dilated to the apex. Protarsi thickened[Endrödi, 1985].

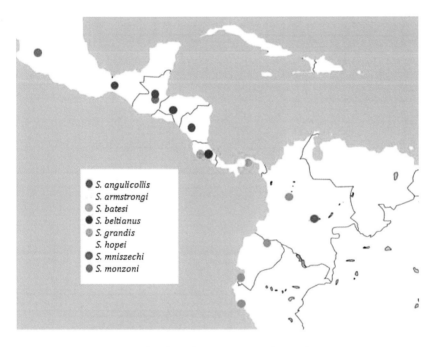

Fig. 98. The distribution map of *Spodistes*.

*Spodistes*의 검색표

1.-머리뿔 끝은 두 갈래로 나뉜다. 그 외에 이빨은 나있지 않다......................6
1'-머리뿔 끝의 뒤에 이빨이 나 있다...2

to 2

to 6

2.-머리뿔 끝은 갈라지지 않는다...3
2'-마리뿔 끝이 두 갈래로 나뉘며 그 뒤에 이빨이 있다..........................4

to 3

to 4

3.-머리뿔의 기부는 삼각형으로 두꺼워진다.............................*beltianus*
3'-머리뿔의 기부는 평평하다..*armstrongi*

beltianus

armstrongi

4.-이마방패가 톱니모양이다...*grandis*
4'-이마방패가 둥글다..5

grandis

to 5

5.-이마방패의 옆 모서리가 두드러진다. 옆면이 강하게 휘어지고, 전흉배판의 옆 테두리는 둥글다...*hopei*
5'-이마방패의 옆 모서리는 두드러지지 않고 옆면은 약하게 휘어진다. 전흉배판이 강하게 각진다...*angulicollis*

 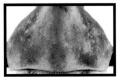

hopei　　　　　　　　　　　　*angulicollis*

6.-머리뿔의 끝 부분이 두 눈 사이의 거리만큼 넓어진다. 전흉배판을 가로지르는, 중심부분의 점각이 강하고 금빛 털이 없는 부분이 있으며 옆 테두리는 두드러지게 각겨있다...*monzoni*
6'-머리뿔의 끝 부분은 두 눈 사이의 거리보다 좁다. 전흉배판은 세로로 좀 더 길고 중심 부분에는 점각이 없으며 금빛 털이 있다. 옆 테두리는 둥글다................7

monzoni　　　　　　　　　　　　to 7

7.-머리에 눈 하나 정도의 길이로 뚜렷한 용골 구조가 머리뿔을 따라 안각에서부터 나있다. 가슴뿔은 앞의 옆면이 평평해 앞의 중심부분에서 강한 용골 구조를, 기부는 단면이 삼각형 모양을 만든다. 머리뿔의 끝 부분은 거의 수직으로 휘어 끝 부분이 두 갈래로 나뉘고, 뒷 방향을 가리킨다...*batesi*
7'-머리에는 안각에서 시작되는 용골구조가 없다. 가슴뿔은 앞면이 둥글고 중심부는 약하게 팽창한 듯 보여 기부는 단면이 반원형이다. 머리뿔의 끝 부분은 두 갈래로 나뉘어 위를 향하며 대형 개체에서는 약하게 두꺼워진다.........*mniszechi*

batesi　　　　　　　　　　　　*mniszechi*

Key to species of *Spodistes*

1.–Cephalic horn bifurcated, without dorsal accessory tooth immediately proximal to apex...6
1'–Cephalic horn with apex simple or bifurcate, with dorsal accessory tooth immediately proximal to apex 2

to 2

to 6

2.–Cephalic horn with apex simple...3
2'–Cephalic horn with apex bifurcate, subapical accessory tooth subspiniform...4

to 3

to 4

3.–Cephalic horn with strong triagular thickening at the base..............*beltianus*
3'–Cephalic horn without triagular thickening at the base.................*armstrongi*

beltianus

armstrongi

4.–Anterior margin of clypeus emarginated...*grandis*
4'–Anterior margin of clypeus rounded...5

grandis

to 5

5.–Lateral angles of clypeus very salient, sides strongly curved, lateral margins of the pronotum regularly rounded..*hopei*
5'–Lateral angles of clypeus scarcely salient, sides slightly curved, lateral margins of the pronotum strongly angulated..*angulicollis*

hopei

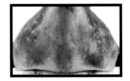

angulicollis

6.–Cephalic horn with apex expanded to about interocular width, fourfifths as wide in smallest individuals, pronotum transverse, distinctly punctate and lacking tomentum medially, with lateral margins noticeably angulate and weakly explanate..*monzoni*
6'–Cephalic horn with apex less expanded, usually less than four-fifths as wide as interocular width; pronotum more elongate medially tomentose and apparently impunctate, with lateral margins round ed..7

monzoni

to 7

7.–Head with short but distinct carina beginning–on ocular canthi and extending perpendicular to lateral clypeal margin, in line with cephalic horn, for about one–half to one ocular width. pronotal horn anterolaterally flattened so that anterior midline forms strong carina and base of horn distinctly triangular in cross section. apex of cephalic horn truncated nearly perpendicular to basal half of horn, apices of bifurcation therefore pointing posteriorly..*batesi*
7'–Head without accessory carina extending from ocular canthi in line with horn. pronotal horn anteriorly rounded, at most with anterior midline weakly tumid, base therefore subsemicircular in cross section, apex of cephalic horn not truncated, apices of bifurcation pointing dorsally, in line with horn, weakly swollen in well developed specimens..*mniszechi*

batesi

mniszechi

Spodistes angulicollis

Dechambre, 1992

묘사. 이마방패가 매우 넓다. 강하게 둥글고, 양 옆의 모서리가 살짝 튀어나와 안각으로 약간 휘어진다. 안각은 넓고 짧다. 머리뿔은 길고 얇은 편이며 위를 향해 휘었다. 두 갈래로 갈라지는 끝 부분에서 뒤를 향하는 이빨이 하나 있다. 전흉배판은 확실히 길기보다는 넓다. 가슴뿔은 원뿔 모양이며 길지 않다. 겉날개는 미세한 점각이 드물게 나있다. 앞 경절은 넓고 세 개의 이빨이 있다. 앞 부절은 두껍고, 마지막 관절이 매우 길다. 안쪽의 발톱이 길고 평평하다[Dechambre, 1992].

분포. 콜롬비아의 아마조나스쪽 지역에 서식한다[Dechambre, 1992].

Description. Clypeus very wide and strongly rounded. Lateral angles slightly protruding, slightly bent up to ocular canthus. Ocular canthus wide and short. Cephalic horn rather long and thin, curved toward top. At base of bifurcation with tooth. Pronotum clearly wider than long. Thoracic horn conic and short. Elytra with fine and sparse punctures. Protibia wide and tridentated. Protarsi thickened, and last joints very long. Inner claw long and flattened[Dechambre, 1992].

Distribution. Amazonian Colombia[Dechambre, 1992].

Fig. 99. Aedeagus of *S. angulicollis*

Colombia, 36 mm, 28 mm
Fig. 100. *Spodistes angulicollis*

Spodistes armstrongi

Dechambre, 1994

묘사. *S. beltianus*와 함께 *Spodistes*의 다른 종과는 머리뿔의 끝이 갈라지지 않는다는 차이점을 가진다[Dechambre, 1994]. *S. beltianus*와는 머리뿔의 기부에 돌기가 없다는 점에서 차이가 있다. 턱에는 두 개의 이빨이 있다. 전흉배판에는 길고 얇은 뿔이 있다. 겉날개는 밀도있고 작은 점각이 있다. 앞 경절은 세 개의 이빨이 있고 앞 부절은 두껍다[Ratcliffe, 2003].

분포. 파나마에 서식한다[Ratcliffe, 2003].

Description. With *S. beltianus*, it is differs from the other species of *Spodistes* by acuminate, non-bifurcated cephalic horn[Dechambre, 1994]. It is separated from *S. beltianus* by the absence of a tubercle at the base of the cephalic horn. Mandibles with two teeth. Pronotum with long, slender horn. Elytra covered with dense, small punctures. Protibia tridentated, and protarsi thickened[Ratcliffe, 2003].

Distribution. Panama[Ratcliffe, 2003].

Cerro Azul, Panama, 37 mm
Fig. 101. *Spodistes armstrongi*

Spodistes batesi

Arrow, 1902

묘사. 머리뿔의 기부 가까이에 넓은 이빨이 있다. 머리의 양 옆에는 안각에서 시작되는 짧고 앞으로 향하는 용골이 있다. 가슴뿔은 뾰족한 이빨이 기부에 있다. 전미절의 소리를 내는 영역은 넓다. 항문상판은 짧고, 짧은 강모가 나있다. 앞 부절은 두껍다[(Endrődi, 1985)].

논의. 산에 인접한 우림 혹은 젖은 숲에서, 600~1600m 고도에서 빛에 유인된다. 우기가 시작될 때 가장 많은 활동을 보인다[(Ratcliffe, 2003)].

분포. 파나마와 코스타리카에 서식한다[(Ratcliffe, 2003)].

Description. Near the base, cephalic horn with a broad tooth. Sides of head with short, forward-directed carina which begins on the ocular canthus. Sharp tooth present at the base of the pronotal horn. Stridulatory area of propygidium short and with very short setae. Protarsi thickened[(Endrődi, 1985)].

Discussion. It is collected at premontane rain forest or wet forest, between 600~1600m, attracted by light. It has a peak of activity at the onset of the rainy season[(Ratcliffe, 2003)].

Distribution. Panama, Costa Rica[(Ratcliffe, 2003)].

AGAOCEPHALINI OF THE WORLD

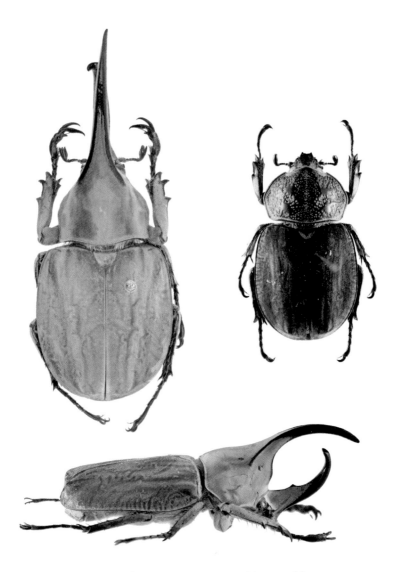

Las Alturas, Costa Rica, 43mm, 28mm

Fig.102. *Spodistes batesi*

Spodistes beltianus
(Bates, 1888)

묘사. *S. armstrongi*와 유사하게, 머리뿔의 끝이 갈라지지 않았다. 그러나 기부에 가깝게, 이빨처럼 확장되어 돌출된 부위가 있다. 이마방패는 둥글다. 가슴뿔은 길고 살짝 굽었으며, 삼각형 돌기가 있다. 전미절에는 뚜렷한 소리를 내는 영역이 없다. 앞 부절은 두껍다[Endrödi, 1985].

분포. 니카라과, 코스타리카에 서식한다[Endrödi, 1985].

Description. Similar to *S. armstrongi*, cephalic horn not bifurcated, but simply acuminated. Area near the basis dilated like a tooth. Clypeus rounded. Pronotal horn long, slightly curved, and with a triangular tooth. There is no distinct stridulatory area at the propygidium. Protarsi thickened[Endrödi, 1985].

Distribution. Nicaragua, Costa Rica[Endrödi, 1985].

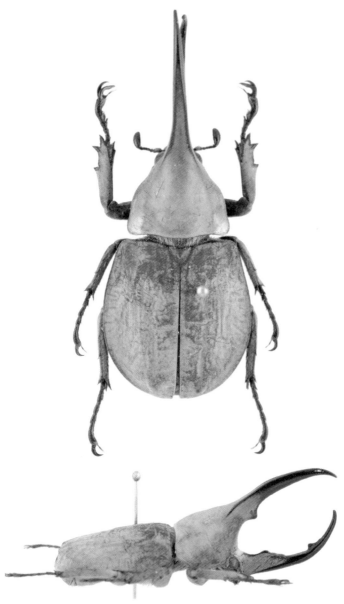

Images courtesy of Calvin Huang.
Fig. 103. *Spodistes beltianus*

Spodistes grandis
Sternberg, 1903

묘사. 이마방패가 넓게 톱니 모양이다. 가슴뿔에는 이빨이 없다. *S. hopei*와 유사하다[(Endrődi, 1985)].

분포. 콜롬비아, 에콰도르에 서식한다.

Description. Clypeus broadly emarginated. Pronotal horn without tooth. It resembles *S. hopei*[(Endrődi, 1985)].

Distribution. Colombia, Ecuador.

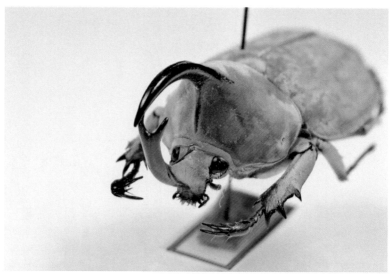

Fig. 104. *Spodistes grandis*

Esmeraldas, Ecuador, 42 mm
Fig. 105. *Spodistes grandis*

Spodistes hopei

Arrow, 1902

묘사. 이마방패의 끝이 둥글다. 항문상판과 배면의 강모가 더욱 짧다. 안각은 짧다. 머리뿔은 대형 개체에서도 비교적 짧다. 머리뿔의 끝 부분이 세 갈래로 나뉜다. 가슴뿔 역시 짧은 편이다[Endrödi, 1985].

분포. 파나마에 서식한다[Endrödi, 1985].

Description. Apex of clypeus rounded. Setae on pygidium and abdomen very short. Ocular canthus short. Cephalic horn short, even in major males. Cephalic horn trifurcated. Pronotal horn also rather short[Endrödi, 1985].

Distribution. Panama[Endrödi, 1985].

Remark

모식표본의 채집 기록이 Granada로 표기되어있어 이 종이 콜롬비아에도 서식하는지 의문이 제기되어왔다. 그러나, 파나마에서만 서식하는 것으로 믿어진다.

The local data of the holotype is just 'Granada', because of that, it is remain questionable whether this species is truly distributed in Colombia. However, the habitats of this species are generally believed Panama.

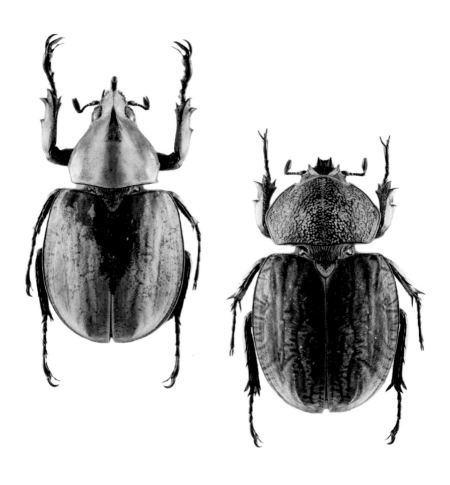

Oeste, Panama, 27 mm, 26 mm

Fig. 106. *Spodistes hopei*

Spodistes mniszechi
(Thomson, 1860)

묘사. 머리뿔에 기부에 희미한 이빨이 있다. 머리의 양 옆에 앞을 향하는 용골이 없다. 앞 경절은 다른 종보다 덜 두껍다. 머리와 가슴뿔은 조금 강하게 휘었다^(Endrödi, 1985).

분포. 중앙아메리카 북부에 서식한다^(Ratcliffe, 2003).

Description. Near the base of cephalic horn indistinctly toothed. No carina at the sides of the head. Protarsi less thickened than the other species. Both horns strongly curved^(Endrödi, 1985).

Distribution. Northern Mesoamerica^(Ratcliffe, 2003)

Fig. 107. *Spodistes mniszechi*

Veracruz, Mexico, 39mm
Fig. 108. *Spodistes mniszechi*

Spodistes monzoni
Warner, 1992

묘사. 전흉배판은 넓고, 디스크는 거친 점각이 있다. 양 옆을 제외하면 표면을 덮는 털이 없다. 양 옆의 가장자리가 각져있다. 뿔은 이빨이 없다. 머리뿔은 두껍고 끝이 깊게 톱니모양이어서 그 넓이가 눈 사이의 거리와 같다[Warner, 1992].

분포. 멕시코, 과테말라, 엘살바도르에 서식한다[Warner, 1992].

Description. Pronotum broad, and its disc coarsely punctated. Except the sides of pronotum, tomentose absent. Horn without internal teeth. Cephalic horn thick, and deeply emarginated at the apex. Apex as wide as dorsal interocular width[Warner, 1992].

Distribution. Mexico, Guatemala, El Salvador[Warner, 1992].

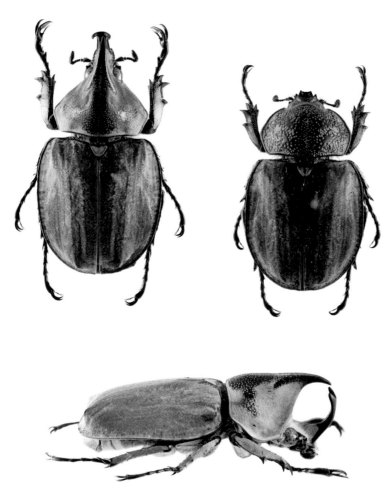

Santa Rosa, Guatemala, 33 mm, 26 mm
Fig. 109. *Spodistes monzoni*

Plate

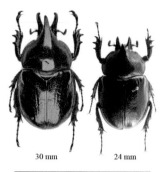

30 mm 24 mm

A. bolboceridus

24 mm

A. diceratops

20 mm

C. bicolor

29 mm

G. bicolor

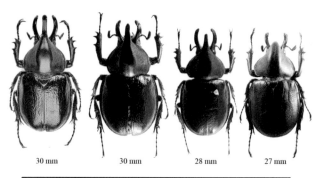

30 mm 30 mm 28 mm 27 mm

A. curvicornis

29 mm
PARATYPE

A. chaminadei

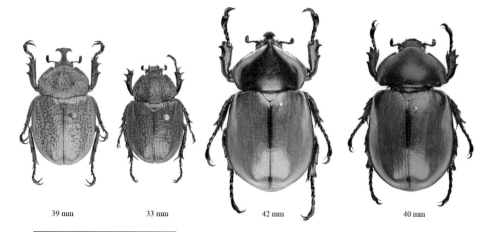

39 mm 33 mm

A. goryi

42 mm 40 mm

M. humboldti

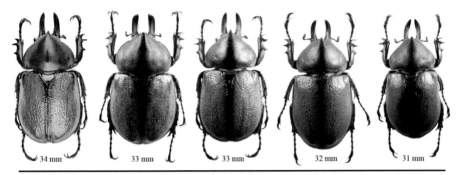

A. cornigera

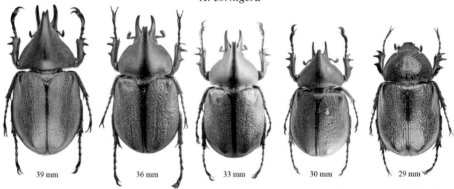

A. mannerheimi

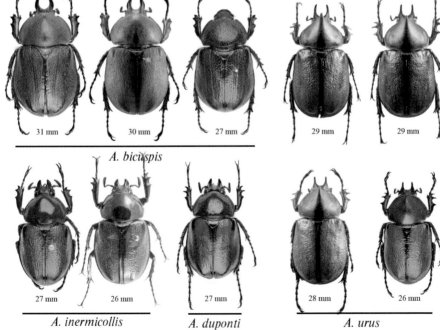

A. bicuspis

A. inermicollis   *A. duponti*   *A. urus*

45 mm

45 mm
PARATYPE

39 mm

32 mm

A. margaridae

24 mm

26 mm

24 mm

21 mm

22 mm

18 mm

M. minicola   *M. elyanae*   *M. matogrossensis*   *M. benjamini*   *M. martinae*

26 mm

30 mm

26 mm

25 mm

M. goyanus   *M. paranensis paranensis*   *M. paranensis lenorae*   *M. mielkeorum*

40 mm

35 mm

30 mm

B. q. quadrimaculatus 40 mm

B. q. tridentiger 40 mm

B. quadrimaculatus quadrimacuatus   *B. quadrimaculatus tridentiger*

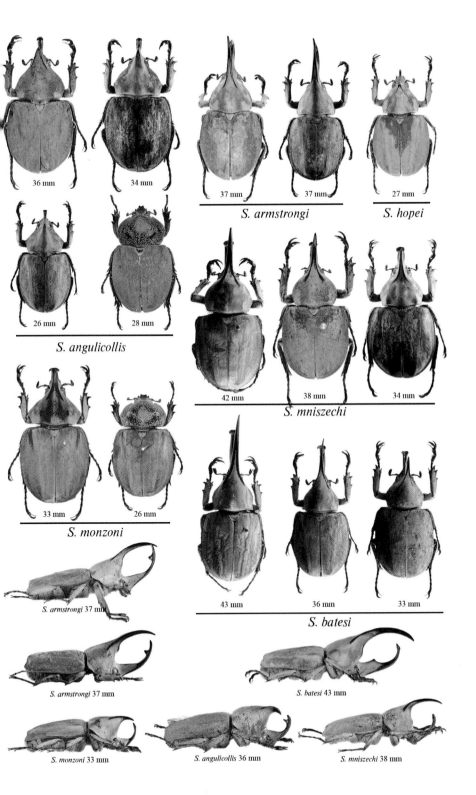

36 mm   34 mm

26 mm   28 mm

S. angulicollis

33 mm   26 mm

S. monzoni

37 mm   37 mm

S. armstrongi

27 mm

S. hopei

42 mm   38 mm   34 mm

S. mniszechi

43 mm   36 mm   33 mm

S. batesi

S. armstrongi 37 mm

S. armstrongi 37 mm

S. batesi 43 mm

S. monzoni 33 mm   *S. angulicollis* 36 mm   *S. mniszechi* 38 mm

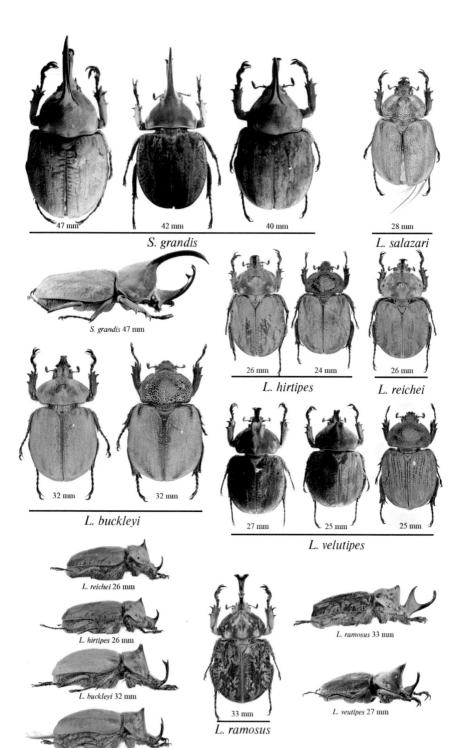

47 mm   42 mm   40 mm

S. grandis

28 mm

L. salazari

S. grandis 47 mm

26 mm   24 mm

L. hirtipes

26 mm

L. reichei

32 mm   32 mm

L. buckleyi

27 mm   25 mm   25 mm

L. velutipes

L. reichei 26 mm

L. hirtipes 26 mm

L. buckleyi 32 mm

S. salazari 28 mm

33 mm

L. ramosus

L. ramosus 33 mm

L. veutipes 27 mm

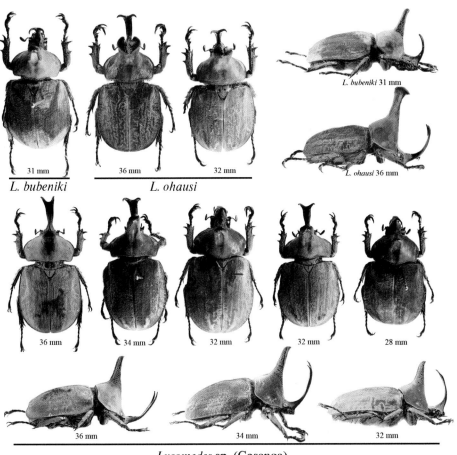

L. bubeniki

L. ohausi

L. bubeniki 31 mm

L. ohausi 36 mm

Lycomedes sp. (Cosanga)

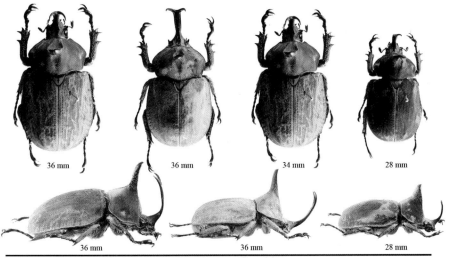

Lycomedes sp. (Carchi)

References

Audinet Serville, M. (1825) Encyclopédie méthodique. Histoire naturelle des animaux

Abadie E.I. (2014) A new species of Brachysiderus Waterhouse, 1881 from Mato Grosso state, Brazil, Lambillionea 114(2):126-127

Abadie E.I., Godinho C.L. & Koike R.M. (2016) A new species of Brachysiderus Waterhouse, 1881 from Goias state, Brazil, Lambillionea 116(3):232-235

Alves, Rafael Sobral (2017) "Revisão de Aegopsis Burmeister, 1847 (Coleoptera, Melolonthidae, Dynastinae)."

Arrow G.J. (1902) Notes and descriptions of some Dynastidae from tropical America, chiefly supplementary to the "Biologia CentraliAmericana", The Annals and Magazine of natural History, including Zoology, Botany and Geology. London 7(10): 137-147

Arrow G.J. (1914) Some further notes on lamellicorn beetles of the subfamily Dynastinae , The Annals and Magazine of natural History, including Zoology, Botany and Geology. London 8(14):257-276, 360

Brett C. Ratcliffe (2003) The Dynastine Scarab Beetles of Costa Rica and Panama (Coleoptera: Scarabaeidae: Dynastinae) Bulletin of the University of Nebraska State Museum.

Burmeister, Hermann (1847) Handbuch der Entomologie

Casey, Thos. L., (1915) Memoirs on the Coleoptera

Castelnau, Francis (1832) Mémoire sur cinquante espèces nouvelles ou peu connues d'insectes, Annales de la Société Entomologique de France, Paris, 1, 404

De Oliveira, Charles Martins, Miguel Angel Morón, and Marina Regina Frizzas.(2008) "Aegopsis bolboceridus (Coleoptera:

Melolonthidae): an important pest on vegetables and corn in Central Brazil." Florida Entomologist 91.2 : 324-327.

Dechambre, R. P. (1992) Nouveaux Dynastidae de la tribu Agaocephalini. Lachaume G. Les Coleopteres Du Monde. Dynastidae Américains Sciences Nat, Venette 14:77-81.

Dechambre R-P (1994) Une nouvelle espèce de Spodistes Burmeister, Revue Francaise d'Entomologie (Nouvelle-Serie) 16(4):149-151

Dechambre, R. P. (1999). Une nouvelle espèce d'Aegopsis Burmeister, 1847. Revue Française d'Entomologie (Nouvelle-Serie) 21(4):173-174.

Endrődi, S. "Horridocalia delislei gen. nov. sp. nov.(Coleoptera: Melolonthidae, Dynastinae)." Folia entomologica hungarica 27 (1974): 49-52.

Endrődi, S. (1970) Monograph of the Dynastinae coleoptera part 3 tribe agaocephalini 4 Acta Zoologica Academiae Scientiarum Hungaricae 16(1-2): 27-96.

Esteban I. Abadie, Paschoal C. Grossi, Pablo S. Wagner (2008) A field guide of the Dynastidae family of the south of South America

Everado Grossi, Agacaphala margaridae, (2008) Livro Vermelho da Fauna Brasileira Ameaçada de Extinção (pp.360-361)

Figueroa, Luis, Brett C. Ratcliffe, and Jhon César Neita-Moreno (2023) "A Review of the Genus Colacus Ohaus, 1910 (Coleoptera: Scarabaeidae: Dynastinae: Agaocephalini) with Description of a New Species from Peru." The Coleopterists Bulletin 77.1 : 58-62.

Grossi E.J. & Dechambre R-P & Grossi P.C. (2012) Une nouvelle sous-espèce de brachysiderus paranensis Arrow, 1902 Coléoptères 18(2):9-12

Laporte, F. (1832) Mémoire sur cinquante espèces nouvelles ou peu connues d'insectes. Annales de la Société entomologique de France. Paris 1:386-415.

Luis Carlos Pardo-Locarno (2020) adiciones a los escarabajos agaocephalini de colombia (coleoptera: melolonthidae: dynastinae)

Martinez, A - Alvarenga, Moacir (1987) Un nuevo subgenero de Agaocephala de Brasil (Col. Scarab. Dynastinae), Anales De La Sociedad Cientifica Argentina, 215, 21-27,

Milani, L. (2017) "Sinopsi del genere Lycomedes Breme (Coleoptera, Scarabaeidae, Dynastinae, Agaocephalini) con ridescrizione de Lycomedes ohausi Arrow maschio, descrizione de Lycomedes ohausi femmina e di una nuova specie dall'Ecuador." Giornale Italiano de Entomologia 14 : 755-774.

Neita-Moreno, J. C. (2015). Revisión del género Colacus Ohaus (Coleoptera: Scarabaeidae: Dynastinae: Agaocephalini). Dugesiana, 22(2), 187-199.

Neita-Moreno, Jhon C., and Brett C. Ratcliffe. (2019) "The Genera of Agaocephalini (Coleoptera: Scarabaeidae: Dynastinae) of Colombia, with Description of a New Species of Lycomedes Brême." The Coleopterists Bulletin 73.4 : 1049-1063.

Ohaus F. (1930) Neue brasilianische Dynastinen Stettiner entomologische Zeitung., Stettin 91:261-265

Pardo-Locarno, Luis Carlos, Alfonso Villalobos Moreno, and Romãn Stechauner Rohringer. (2015) "Nueva especie de Lycomedes Bréme, 1844 (Coleoptera: Melolonthidae: Dynastinae) de los Andes colombianos y clave para identificación de las especies." Insecta Mundi.

Ratcliffe, B. C., & Cave, R. D. (2011) Revisions of the Genera Endroedianibe Chalumeau and Hispanioryctes Howden and Endrödi (Coleoptera: Scarabaeidae: Dynastinae) from Hlspaniola, with Descriptions of New Species. The Coleopterists Bulletin, 65(1), 1-14.

Ratcliffe, B. C., Cave, R. D., & Paucar-Cabrera, A. (2020) The Dynastine Scarab Beetles of Ecuador:(Coleoptera: Scarabaeidae: Dynastinae). University of Nebraska State Museum.

Ratcliffe, B.C.; Cave, R.D.; Le Tirant, S. (2023) The Dynastine Scarab Beetles of Argentina, Paraguay, and Uruguay (Coleoptera: Scarabaeidae: Dynastinae). University of Nebraska.

Smith, A. B. (2006) A review of the family-group names for the superfamily Scarabaeoidea (Coleoptera) with corrections to nomenclature and a current classification. The Coleopterists Bulletin, 60(mo5), 144–204.

Sobral, R., JW, D. M., & Grossi, P. C. (2019) A new species of Colacus Ohaus, 1910 (Coleoptera: Scarabaeidae: Dynastinae) from the Mata Seca biotope of Brazil, and notes on Colacus morio Ohaus, 1910. Zootaxa, 4695(2), zootaxa–4695.

Sobral, Rafael, Paschoal C. Grossi, and Jose W. De Morais. (2018) "Two new species of Aegopsis Burmeister, 1847 (Coleoptera: Scarabaeidae: Dynastinae) from the central Brazilian Cerrado." Zootaxa 4526.2 : 175–194.

Thomson J. (1860) Agaocephalitarum Synopsis, Musée Scientifique ou Recueil d'Histoire Naturelle. Paris 1:14–19

Warner, William B. (1992) "A new north American Spodistes Burmeister (Coleoptera: Scarabaeidae)." The Coleopterists' Bulletin : 378–383.